YOGA

Swami Venkatesananda

FOREWORDS BY:

The Vatican
Archbishop George Appleton
Rabbi Joseph H. Gelberman, Ph.D.
Pir Vilayat Khan

Published by
THE CHILTERN YOGA TRUST (AUSTRALIA)
P.O. BOX 2 SOUTH FREMANTLE 6162
WESTERN AUSTRALIA

6th Edition — 1983

7th Edition - 2001

ISBN O-9590690-6-2

Printed by
QUALITY PRESS
9 ROBERTS STREET WEST,
OSBORNE PARK, 6017
WESTERN AUSTRALIA

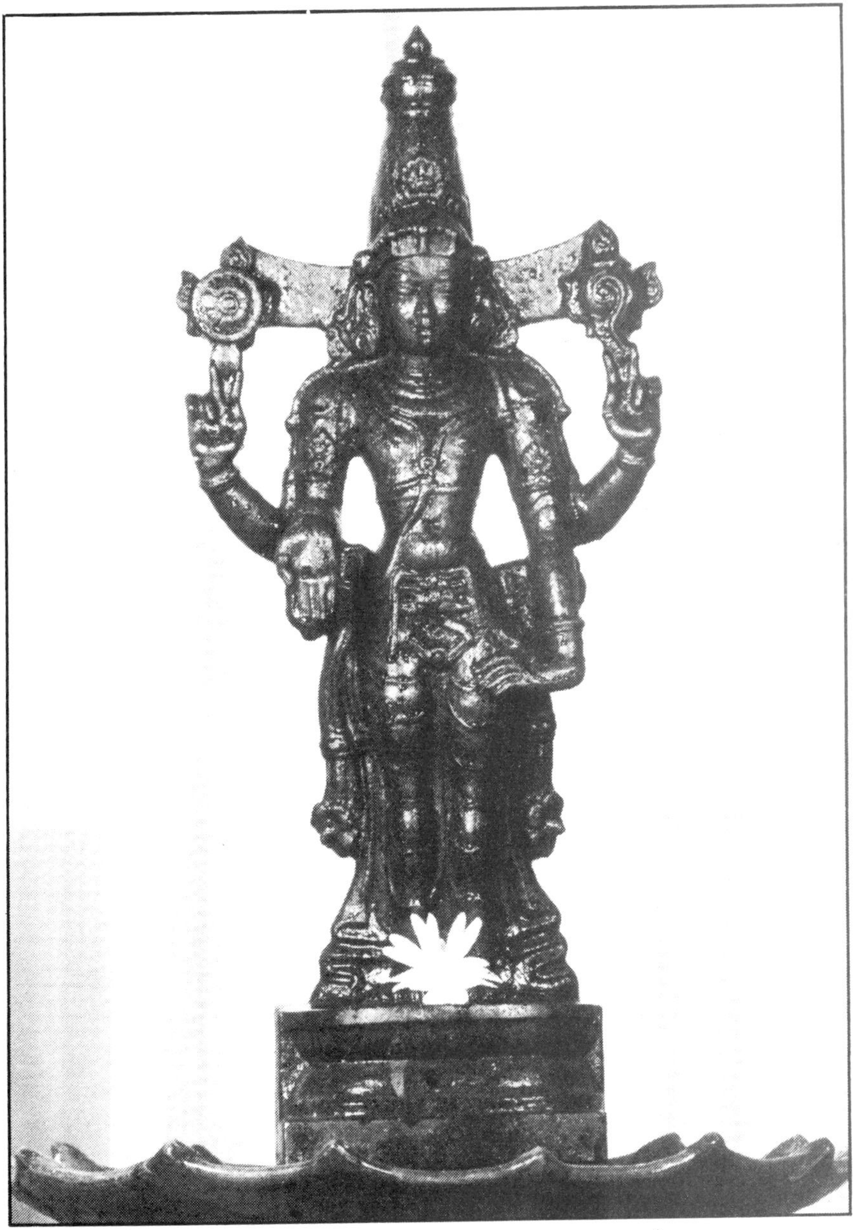

DEDICATED TO LORD VEṄKAṬEŚA

Swami Venkatesananda receiving the blessings of Swami Sivananda.

PREFACE

During the first part of my stay in South Africa in 1961, I noticed an intense desire on the part of many Indians and non-Indians to rediscover for adoption in their own lives a saner value of life. The impact of materialistic civilisation made it difficult for them to assimilate orthodox teaching as offered in the scriptures; and they were not quite satisfied with a complete break-away from tradition into the free-thinker's bye-lanes where all but the chosen few lose their path altogether. For their benefit I prepared a pamphlet – "The Handbook of Yoga" – explaining the orthodox principles in simpler style, without, however, deviating from tradition. The response was very encouraging.

When I was in Mauritius in 1963, Mr K.L. Dassagne of the "Mauritius Times" asked me to contribute a series of articles on Yoga. I based these articles on the former pamphlet, considerably expanding the thoughts, to make them clearer. The results were still more encouraging. I offer my grateful thanks to Mr Dassagne and the editor of the "Mauritius Times", the hon. Mr B. Ramallah for allowing me the hospitality of their paper.

Since my return to Mauritius in April 1964, I have been repeatedly asked to publish all the articles in book form. I have put them all together and added a few more to make the book comprehensive, and offer it at the feet of the lord who dwells in the hearts of all earnest seekers after him.

S.V.

PREFACE TO THE SIXTH EDITION

To meet continuing demand for this text, both here in Australasia and overseas we are reprinting this complete edition of 'Yoga'.

We are grateful to Swami Lakṣmi Ananda for preparing the manuscript, to Joan Levy for the excellent Yoga Asana photographs taken by her during my visit to Buffalo in 1977, to Swami Śobha for typing the the whole book for the press, to Jan Rolfe for the artwork, to Leonie for her assistance, to David for layout, photographics, printing and folding and to Janet for the collating.

We are indebted to Mr Eric Powell, Editor of the '*Fremantle Gazette*' for his continued generosity towards the Chiltern Yoga Trust.

S.V.

BLESSINGS FROM THE VATICAN

A Few Words of True Friendship

I had the pleasure of meeting twice in Rome, at a few years' interval, the master of rāja yoga Swami Venkatesananda. We conversed together on that which is our common quest: to seek oneself and to help man find the divine. I could only admire how much we were in accord on many points, particularly on those concerning the path, despite deep differences.

When the Swami asked me for a word of introduction for the reprinting of the books written by him on integral yoga, I willingly accepted this invitation; and this is the purpose of the few words that follow.

We christians learn in the Bible that god made us for him and made us in his image, that this image is engraved like a seal on our hearts, and that though this image has been veiled by sin, there is just enough revelation of it to orientate ourselves towards god as the fulfilment of our existence and the absolute goal of our search for happiness. As St. Paul said, god has created us "to look for the deity, to reach it, if possible, as a blind groping person would" (Acts 17:27): and St. Augustine expresses his own experience as follows: "You have created us for you, lord, and our heart remains restless until it rests in you." And the Swami, speaking of the origin of raja yoga, tells us that it gushes simply from the hunger for god which each man feels: "When he hungers for god, he develops his own technique, and that is yoga". (Rāja Yoga For The Youth, p.2)

In fact, this pain of separation from god, this hunger for him, is felt by all people and each one has looked, in his own manner, for a remedy to this hunger. But India is, perhaps, the country where during the course of the past thirty centuries incalculable generations of sages did not want to give their lives any goal other than this: viz., to search for the path and its integral transmission, to obtain the peace of the heart by mastering the senses, to purify and simplify the spirit by the rejection of vain desires, and to concentrate the spirit in austerity. They also teach us, in their way, that "the kingdom of god is within" (Luke 17:21), that you can get it by sacrificing all the rest (Matthew 13:46) and that "our eye should become pure so that our whole body is enlightened by it" (Matthew 6:22). If the points of departure and arrival of our research seem different according to our intellectual categories, in the view of god who sees the entire universe, there is unity. We know that the natural law, the Mosaic Law and the evangelic law, in perfectioning one another do not cancel one another and remain fundamentally one – looking within ourselves in order to reach him, if possible, in himself.

We should not be surprised by the analogies (which also illustrate the path) to which the swami resorts by citing the scriptures that he knows so well. It is possible (and helpful) for everyone to utilise the treasure of psychological and spiritual experience for his own progress and to enable him to understand god better. Speaking of another Indian method of quest which is dhyana or the zen of the Japanese, a master of this discipline said to a catholic missionary who wanted to expound christian zen as a method of spirituality more adapted to the far east: "Zen is a method; it is like a railroad track on which you can launch all the trains that you want." One could say as much or even more, of rāja yoga, the discipline of sages who have renounced everything to devote themselves solely to the divine. These sages have noble and useful lessons to give not only to the christians of their own race, but also to all our modern societies which see no more than the form and the technique and seem to have forgotten the true reason for the existence of man, which is the key to his happiness.

We would be mistaken, however, if we think that we shall find an easy way in rāja yoga: as in the christian spirituality, one obtains facility through a long and arduous struggle, by renouncing everything which is not the absolute. But, then, as in our case, the initial struggle is compensated by the inspiration of continuously growing divine love.

To know all these ways and to use them when necessary is also a better way of understanding the deep fraternity of man. It will promote mutual understanding, respect, and mutual help among the people. For, this, too, let us be thankful to Swami

Venkatesananda for placing so excellently the noble treasures of hindu spirituality within our reach, through his books published in our languages.

P. Humbertclaude.

P. HUMBERTCLAUDE
Secretary-General
Secretariat for non-christians

From the VATICAN. June 11, 1970.

SECRETARIAT OF STATE
No. 216.554

From the Vatican. 26 August 1972

Dear Swami Venkatesananda,

I have been directed by the Holy Father to acknowledge the gift of a copy of your book, "Yoga", which you presented to him during your recent audience.

His Holiness is grateful for the gift and for the sentiments of devotion which prompted this gesture.

As a sign of his appreciation, the Holy Father invokes upon you blessings from God.

With good wishes, I remain

Yours sincerely,

Swami Venkatesananda
C/- Postmaster-General
Mauritius

BLESSING

From The Archbishop in Jerusalem
Telephone 87708
Telegrams:
Angleps, Jerusalem

St George's Close
P.O. Box 1248–Jerusalem

I am grateful to my friend Swami Venkatesananda for visiting me in Western Australia and in Jerusalem, and for a copy of his book YOGA, from which I have learned much to help me in my discipline of meditation. A re-reading of this book has reminded me of the control of breath and posture which can help to quieten body and mind for deeper peace of spirit.

+ George Appleton.

George Appleton
Anglican Archbishop in Jerusalem

Easter 1973

FOREWORD

It was a rare spiritual encounter meeting Swami Venkatesananda and it will always remain vivid in my memory and consciousness with a special significance. When I listened to, and exchanged dialogue with him at many meetings and retreats where we appeared together his beautiful simplicity coupled with abounding wisdom, immediately makes itself manifest. This double essence of scholarship and humanity make Swami Venkatesananda an outstanding teacher. Martin Buber would have called him "a MENSH", meaning freely, a man of quality in all areas.

In translating this insight and simplicity into his book on Yoga, we get the same inspiration and wisdom from his words as he points out ways to live out and act out the principles of Yoga in the mainstream of living.

His book, interestingly enough, points out similarities to the old movement of Hassidism, and the more current aspect of NEO-HASSIDISM within the Jewish religion which emphasizes worship through JOY, the SINCHA concept, worship through SERVICE, the AVODAH concept, and worship through PURPOSE, or the KAVANAH concept. These relate to the faith, acts, and discipline that Swamiji describes so eloquently in his book. When he describes the quest for happiness, meditation and service, it relates to the psychological, existential formula for living and growing on a three-rung "Psycho-Social-Spiritual" basis. This refers to the I—ME level of personal insight to self-defeating defenses and mechanisms on the unconscious level, with the commitment of finding out "WHO AM I' " and "WHAT AM I FEELING." It further refers to the I—YOU level of social obligation or my commitment to my fellowman and society or "HOW DO I LOVE" and "HOW DO I GIVE". Finally, it refers to the I—THOU level of spiritual involvement or my dedication to God and my cosmic role in perfecting creation as a partner to God.

Swami Venkatesananda has related powerfully to these basic issues in his book by summing up his teachings on Yoga as promoting "discipline, faith, and social solidarity".

The readers will find this book a personal, and spiritual guide and lesson for life enhancement.

In spiritual fellowship, personal inspiration, and deep respect, I relate to this book on Yoga and to Swami Venkatesananda with gratitude.

Rabbi Joseph H. Gelberman
The Little Synagogue
27 East 20th Street
New York, New York 10003

July 15, 1974

FOREWORD

Yoga has become a household word in the West. For the 'pitr' – – the ancestor in Indian folk thinking, it was likened to the yoke that connects the energy of the ox to its charge, and so universally yoga is the connecting link harnessing untapped cosmic energy into transforming productivity in man. Much of the secret of tapping the inexhaustible sources of energy in the far reaches of the human compass remains mysteriously concealed by the adepts, partly as a precaution to shield the people of good faith from the apprentice-sorcerer volunteers unaware of the many uncanny implications of unleashing a thunderbolt in a fragile conductor. But every now and again, the area of this science unveiled to the public extends a little further, and Swami Venkatesananda is an explorer while being a traditionalist and knows how to wrap mysterious know-hows into the trappings of mirth to sidetrack the curiosity of dilettants and edify the adepts. The book is a thrilling discovery if one reads both the words and what lies between them.

Pir Vilayat Khan
Head of Sufi Order

INTRODUCTION

In the western world today wherever the idea that yoga is magic has been dispelled, it is regarded as a unique and unparalleled system of physical culture (which it is) and nothing more (which is it not). People who are anxious to save on doctor's bills, women who are figure-conscious, good-livers who yet want to escape from the tension inherent in their way of life – these people practise yoga, but they ignore the fundamental thesis in yoga, the unity of body-mind-spirit.

The yogi believes in the ideal of a 'sound mind in a sound body' but that is because he knows that body and mind are basically one, a single unit with two poles as it were, that what happens in one inevitably reflects in and affects the other. Yet his ultimate aim is not a 'body perfect', because he knows that the body itself is subject to decay and decomposition. It is an instrument, worth keeping in good working order while the work lasts. It is a vehicle best to maintain well till it takes him to his destination. The destination is described as self-realisation.

The brain

The path to self-realisation has been well and beautifully laid by our ancients. To begin with the physical body is well trained, yet the student of yoga does not pay too much attention to the body's musculature. Yoga postures exert a profound and salutary influence upon the internal vital organs of the body. Right from here the genius of yoga becomes apparent. Special attention is devoted to that part of the physical and vital anatomy which distinguishes man from the animal kingdom, the brain. Man possesses a highly developed and complex brain; he only possesses it, but does not always use it! Disused brain atrophies! Gerontologists have discovered that one of the principal causes of failing intellectual powers associated with senility is decreased blood supply to the brain. Hence, one of the most famous of yoga postures, the śiras āsana or the headstand keeps the brain cells charged with energy. It is naturally reputed to arrest mental senility, to improve memory and to preserve intellectual faculties from being impaired even in ripe old age.

Taking advantages of the earth's gravitational pull, the yogi's heart pours an abundant supply of blood into his head, re-charging the cells, strengthening the vital organs in the head, such as the eyes and the ears, nourishing the all-important endocrine glands, the pineal and the pituitary. The latter in conjunction with the other glands of the endocrine system is responsible for the emotional balance or imbalance of the personality, and hence the yogi enjoys a balanced personality. Almost all of the yoga postures (loosely called exercises) are woven around the backbone to ensure its flexibility and strength. If the backbone is supple, the central nervous system is strong and the psychic force called prāṇa circulates freely, preventing disease and promoting well-being. Some postures look after the endocrine glands. Others squeeze, massage and relax the other vital organs of the body like the abdominal viscera, the lungs and the limbs.

Beyond mind and body

Modern psychosomatic medicine is beginning to recognise the intimate relationship between mental or emotional states and disease. A tense nervous system and hormonal imbalance brought about by stress and strain, wrong thinking and ill-feeling, can expose the physical body to germs and viruses, whereas a strong nervous system and hormonal balance maintained by the practice of yoga, which includes psychological and emotional order, can neutralise the effects of germs and viruses. Moreover, one who is tense tends to grip and hold these germs and viruses within him!

Yoga promotes well-being. But, this is not just absence of illness. It is a condition that really transcends the body and the mind. This is the purpose of yoga. An athlete or gymnast exercises the body in order proudly to display it; a yogi exercises the body in order to discover the marvellous intelligence that is built into it. An unhealthy body houses a distracted mind which is obsessed by the malfunctioning of the diseased organ. In fact, such malfunctioning is the fruit of man's ignorance of and crime against the intelligence that fills every cell of the body: when the mind or the will does not interfere, this intelligence functions perfectly (for instance, in deep sleep), and when there is ego-interference and consequent disturbance in balance, the adjustment that the intelligence makes in order to restore the balance is what is popularly known as physical or psychological malfunction or illness. The yogi, while practising the yoga postures discovers this astounding truth: this inner intelligence is beyond the mind and the ego, and he cannot 'add a cubit to his stature by taking a thought'. A healthy body looks after itself, freeing his mind for other, more serious work.

Once the yogi is established in this state of well-being, he is able to pursue his spiritual goal unaffected by even physical illness which may be occasioned by other 'natural' factors. His body looks after itself, and he looks towards his spiritual goal.

Perhaps this is what 'mind over matter' means: here, the 'mind' does not refer to the thinking faculty, but to that which is beyond it, beyond the 'me'. This intelligence at once pervades the mind and the body and, therefore, transcends both of them. It is often known as the self, the spirit, the higher mind, the soul or the indwelling presence.

If the physical part of yoga has been carefully, systematically and diligently practised, the yogi's mind would naturally be calm and his emotions under control, yet it will not do to take these for granted. Yoga involves strict mental and emotional (moral) discipline, too. While certain breathing exercises called prāṇāyāma aid the yogi in his control of thought and emotion, he is advised to watch them in their own spheres. The physical practices of yoga without the corresponding effort to control the mind and the emotions fail to achieve anything; because while the yoga postures tend toward psychological and emotional order, the wilful disturbance of that order in the psychological sphere neutralises the benefit. Unmindful of this the student of yoga complains that he has made no progress.

When the intelligent control over the mind and the emotion goes hand-in-hand with the physical postures of yoga and the breathing exercises, the yogi very soon achieves an indescribable peace of mind. This is the very opposite of drug-induced peace. The peace of mind that the yogi enjoys is characterised by a conscious experience of inner power, and a powerful experience of consciousness. A still mind reflects the inner spirit in all its divine majesty.

The disturbed mind is opaque. The still mind is transparent; and the light of the spirit is radiated through it without the least distortion.

Meditation

The grandeur of the spirit that the yogi senses during the preliminary yoga practices compels him to meditate deeply. Unobstructed by evil thoughts, undistracted by emotions, with the body and mind perfectly harmonised, the yogi dives deep within himself and enjoys profound meditation. In meditation he discovers that the spirit in him is the reality. It is the spirit that lends power to his mind and life to his body. When body, mind and spirit are harmonised through yoga, the spirit functions through the mind and body without impediment. In such a harmonised state, the yogi's attitude to his outer life changes drastically. He is able to view the world in a dispassionate, objective way. He is freed from the earthy currents and crosscurrents of conflicting ideas and feelings. He is able to appreciate life better. He is able to understand others better. He is happy in all conditions, for his happiness does not depend upon others. He is peaceful in all conditions, for his peace springs from within himself. By persistent and diligent practice, he attains self-realisation which is a synonym for freedom or salvation.

Yoga is not a self-centred psycho-physical discipline to be undertaken in a Himalayan cave, in an African jungle or in the cloistered isolation of a hermitage. It may make use of all of these. It may make use of places of worship like the temple, church, mosque or meditation chamber. But to confine yoga to any of these is like clenching one's fist in an attempt to capture the wind: sheer delusion.

The yogi's self is not the limited self-asserting personality, the vain ego which regards itself as a distinct entity whose interests are constantly threatened by everyone else in this world, and which transforms life into a constant struggle for survival. The yogi's self is not an island perilously floating on the ocean called the world, but is the bed of the ocean itself, the substratum for the world and infinite individuals. The yogi's self is the self of all, a spiritual principle which knows no dividing walls.

In fact this is the ultimate aim and purpose of even such seemingly isolationist practices as meditation. We meditate in order to discover the self. Even as this is glimpsed, it is revealed to us that this self is the self of all. If, during meditation, it shines within us, it is because we had deliberately closed our eyes upon the universe, no doubt with a valid reason. After meditation, we open our eyes and realise that the self is the indwelling omnipresence. "I am the self of all," is the actual direct realisation of the yogi.

Thus the yogi becomes the living embodiment of the great commandments of lord Jesus. In fact, to me, a hindu, the holy cross itself symbolises the threefold commandment of lord Jesus, and therefore the very essence of yoga. The vertical beam of the holy cross symbolises the commandment: Love thy god – god who is above, beyond the reach of the intellect, and who is below, deep within one's own being. The horizontal beam of the holy cross symbolises the other two commandments: Love thy neighbour and love thy enemy. The friend on the right and the enemy on the left are both our neighbours. Thus is our consciousness united to our god and to our neighbour.

Hence, my master Swami Sivananda insisted that meditation and service of humanity go hand in hand. One acts as the touchstone of the other. St. Paul declared that he who said that he loved god and who yet hated his neighbour was a liar. When the self is realised in deep meditation, it reveals itself to us as the self of all. In our daily life this is translated as unselfish service and love. This is the acid test. If such loving service does not ceaselessly flow from us, we are still far from the goal of yoga and the meditation is imperfect if not actually delusion and self-deception. There still is a lot of impurity covering the heart, distorting the vision of the self. This impurity is worn out by the deliberate practice of unselfishness and love in our daily life. My master therefore demanded that all these should be combined in our practice of yoga and he summed up the ideal of integral yoga in his famous four words: Serve, love, meditate, realise.

Inner harmony and social adjustment

Yoga pays immediate dividends. The physical part of yoga improves our health, frees us from tensions and diseases and confers a state of well-being on us. It enables us to acquire progressively increasing control over our mind and our emotions. This control in its turn greatly aids the social aspect of yoga which leads to a healthy social adjustment. We are really able to understand everyone, even our enemies.

This understanding is very different from supercilious tolerance with its air of superiority. It is different from even a higher state of social relationship where we love our neighbours on an equal footing. It is true understanding – standing under the other person, magnifying him, appreciating his stand from a new angle. This is the divine love which Krishna, Buddha, and Jesus commanded us to cultivate. This is what yoga confers upon us.

Harmony is the aim of yoga. The yogi recognises that harmony is one and indivisible. Harmony in society is possible only if the members of that society and particularly its leaders are harmonised within themselves. If the leader does not enjoy peace within himself, he will disturb the peace of his followers and the entire society will be frequently churned into a turmoil.

Even in our own individual lives and in our own domestic spheres, yoga (by generating, promoting and preserving inner harmony) confers freedom from psychosomatic disorders of the body and the mind, and ensures good adjustment. Dr Abraham Sperling in his book on psychology says: "Only insight into one's true motives can ensure good adjustment. And, as insight is the best therapy, it is the best preventive." Insight is seeing from within – seeing from within the other man, and seeing the mind from within itself.

What prevents this insight? Moral blindness, the darkness of ignorance and the unsteadiness of our vision. Yoga is designed just to remove these factors. Yoga enables us to purify our heart and mind. Yoga teaches us the science of concentration and meditation. Yoga enables us to come face to face with our own self which is the self of all. In meditation when the mind is still and does not bring up to the surface hidden anxieties and cravings, the self is perceived in its true light as the reflection of the cosmic being or god.

There are numerous techniques for concentration of the mind and meditation. Yet there are some people who mistake deep thinking for meditation, or who regard prayer and meditation as synonymous. The fault is not theirs. It is difficult to describe meditation. It is possible to indicate only what it is not. It is not thinking. It is not prayer. It is not absent-mindedness. It is not sleep.

Great men meditate

Great men in every field resort to meditation. Poets and painters, scientists and saints experience meditation in their life: they declare that their masterpieces were received by them from some other source. When their minds were stilled by bewilderment, shock, wonder or devotion, the divine within granted them a vision of truth. They had a glimpse of the majesty of the self, the grandeur of god within. This glimpse was later clothed by them in the garments of their own distinctive faculties: the poet and the painter give the world their masterpieces, the scientist and the saint describe the truth in their own words.

Each of them uses his own equipment. Yoga needs no external props, but utilises one's own inner equipment. This is the only difficulty. True, even the poet, the painter and the scientist have to discipline themselves to acquire the qualification necessary for them to obtain that inspiration which eventually made them great. But the discipline was partly control of instruments outside themselves and partly inner discipline. In the case of the saint or the yogi, the discipline is entirely subjective, discipline of the body and the mind. He has to study his mind with his own mind and yet be objective and scientific. He has to discover the higher mind within and with it control the lower mind, without the aid of a psychoanalyst or psychiatrist. In this inner struggle, he may use symbols and techniques; but he should beware of turning the means into ends. He has to be constantly vigilant and avoid the temptation to stop short of the goal. His goal is self-realisation. His goal is perfect integration of his personality, integration of himself with his neighbours, and ultimately integration of his individuality with the cosmic being.

This is yoga. It destroys the very roots of disharmony and maladjustment, of cravings and anxieties, of sin and suffering. Physical well-being and mental relaxation, peace of mind and purity of heart, brilliance of intellect and illumination of the very soul of man are some of the fruits of yoga. It does not disturb social solidarity but promotes it. It does not disturb one's religious faith but strengthens it. It demands nothing but your willingness to discipline yourself and sincere application of its psycho-physical methods of self-culture.

CONTENTS

Chapter One
DIVINE LIFE

Chapter Two
KARMA YOGA

Chapter Three
BHAKṬI YOGA

Chapter Four
HAṬHA YOGA

Chapter Five
RĀJĀ YOGA

Chapter Six
JÑĀNA YOGA

Chapter One

DIVINE LIFE

1. *THE WORLD WE LIVE IN*

Man has endeavoured through the ages to live without God or the cosmic Being. Political philosophers, economists and scientific 'sages' have assigned to themselves the godly role of protecting man's peace and happiness, while others function as religious leaders, offering easy salvation to their supporters. Politics, science and economics have failed. Let man now turn towards God. If the religious spirit is absent from our life it has no value, but once it is added then learning, wealth, social position, political or scientific leadership can all assume meaning and purposefulness.

The word 'ḍharma' means "a factor that sustains, upholds, protects and brings together". It brings us all together, binds us in a wonderful and divine cord of love; that is what religion means. Anyone using this ḍharma or religion to divide society into antagonistic groups is spreading irreligion and doing the greatest harm to this ḍharma. Ultimately ḍharma unites us with god; god who dwells in all beings.

Thus our religion or ḍharma ought to promote the prosperity of mankind and also ensure the salvation of man. By keeping us together in a bond of love, we are almost compelled to serve one another and thus promote one another's interests and welfare. By uniting us with god, we are liberated from pettiness, worldliness, selfishness and greed. Here is the greatest miracle on earth: the silent transformation of the human heart, which our ḍharma brings about. It reminds us that we form the one body of god, inseparably united in him. We may have our own characteristics, faculties, and temperament; we may follow different paths to him, but in his love we are all united, and eventually we shall all reach his feet. All our efforts for the betterment of the lot of mankind fail only because we have not yet realised this.

Religion has suffered the same fate as the present era – that of distortion. The simple is made complex. Yet we see on the horizon the dawn of the age of simplicity, and of an urge to seek for the truth in a maze of distortions. Even the word 'yoga' has been distorted. Yoga has nothing to do with miracles and magic, but is the synonym of its phonetic cousin 'yoke', which is the essential meaning of the word 'religion'. Yoke unites two, religion binds them.

Distortion has also crept into religion and divided mankind into opposing camps of 'your religion' and 'my religion'. True religion (yoga) ignores this disharmony and yokes all of us together for humanweal. The source scriptures of all religions say that we should love our neighbour as ourselves and that we should love God with all our being. That is yoga and that is religion. The two must be linked.

Understood aright, therefore, yoga can enrich our life and fulfil its purpose. By yoking us, uniting us and binding us together with a cord of love, it indirectly promotes harmony, peace and prosperity. God is love. The soul yoked to god is possessed and led by this love. We are all bound by the cord of his love which is the omnipresent omnipotence that creates, sustains and redeems all.

That is theory, and theory must be translated into practice. Fundamentally, yoga is simple. It demands the curbing of our egoism, annihilation of selfishness and effective control of our mind and senses, so that they function in tune with the infinite. In practice however, we discover that before we attempt to harmonise the self with society and with god, we should strive to integrate our personality so that our thought, word and deed, as also our intellect, emotion and life, do not tear us into several disjointed personalities. Yoga integrates our personality by revealing our own inner nature, its potentialities and limitations.

By an interesting process of social service, worship by god, inward contemplation and health giving physical posture and breathing exercises, yoga achieves the greatest of all miracles – the transformation of the human heart.

2. *THE MEANING OF LIFE*

What is the meaning of life? Why are we born as human beings? Do we merely exist until we die? What is my relation with you? Why do I suffer and why am I happy sometimes? What is the meaning of the terms 'pleasure' and 'pain'?

These and similar questions occur to many of us at some time or other in our life, but the tragedy is that they do not arise in the mind of many people until they are rudely shaken by some shock, loss or calamity. They were sleeping and hence they were unaware of the meaning of life and the facts of existence. There are some who do not even wake up after many unhappy experiences in life!

The 'normal' man in the modern world is far too busy with the struggle for existence to find time for such thoughts about life. He is content merely to exist, he hardly lives. There comes a stage in ignorance, when it is mistaken for knowledge or wisdom; like a long-caged bird that has forgotton its very birthright to soar into the sky, and which fights to remain in its cage, man hugs ignorance and limitation. Even misery fails to awaken him: he changes his tactics, blames his neighbours and endeavours to find happiness by other methods.

In this process of awakening, there are two ways open to us. If we heed the precepts of the master Swami Sivananda, we can be spiritually healed and awakened which is the easy way. But if we ignore his message, god has to resort to other methods to bring home to us the truth that we live in a world of pain and death and that we cannot find real happiness here. Sooner or later, the easy or difficult way, we have to ask ourselves the great question: 'What is the meaning of life '? Hence our master used to sing:

Is there not a nobler mission than eating,
drinking and sleeping?
It is difficult to get a human birth, therefore try your
best to realise (god) in this birth.

It is good to keep these flaming words of wisdom ever before us so that our life may be illumined by the light of our master's life and teachings. Life has a great mission: it is to find god who is supreme bliss. Life minus limitation or conditioning is bliss: this is the meaning of life. Its discovery is yoga.

3. QUEST OF HAPPINESS

In man's heart there is an unceasing, but paradoxically urgent urge for pleasure and happiness. In fact, this is the urge to immortality and it is this urge that has led him up the ladder of evolution to his present human birth. But it is not correctly understood. When there is the cry of restlessness in the heart of man, he does not always discern the right cause.

No living being is satisfied with merely living. If we merely had to exist, life would be easy. There is this continuous quest for happiness. That is the meaning of life, that is the nature of our self.

Happiness is within your own self. You fail to get it only because you are searching for it where it does not exist. The common and universal experience of deep sleep is proof that this happiness is within us. This sleep is the only period of the day when we are really happy, free from worry and anxiety. Moreover in sleep we "rest within ourselves" and get new energy!

What is it that prevents us from enjoying this happiness constantly? Because of ignorance, the little 'I' is unable to find its way consciously to this inner source, and therefore it endeavours to find that happiness in the external objects of the world, which it can see, grasp and experience.

Man has scaled the highest peak and delved deep into the bowels of the earth, but he does not know what is within himself. And within him is god, the fountain of joy and bliss, the goal of his quest.

It is through a deliberate turning away from the objects of pleasure in this world and by the practice of meditation that the seeker after truth enters the inner realm consciously and with full awareness. But this 'turning away' should not be construed to mean 'running away'. It is like averting our gaze from a glaring object; it hurts the eye, until we put on sunglasses, when we can enjoy that very sight which previously hurt us. We turn our gaze away from the objects of the world for a little while until we are able to adjust our inner vision and look at the world through the eyes of god. Then the world is no longer a painful process of birth and death, but a charming field of divine activity. The very same world, seen through god's eyes, appears as it is – the body of god, which is good.

In the synthesis of activity and idealism, of dynamism and divinity, lies the secret of yoga. Yoga is contemplative dynamism. It implies neither running away nor even turning permanently away from the world, but looking through it and perceiving god who is the reality underlying the world.

4. THE FIRST PRINCIPLE OF YOGA

The deluded man is sure that his happiness is derived from the objects of the world, until pain awakens him to the truth that pain is the result of the enjoyment, whereas the happiness was derived from within himself when the mind ceased to restlessly long for pleasure.

Sleep not only gives us the clue to the great truth that happiness is within us, but also provides us with the two vital laws that govern its experience, viz. forget the world and forget self. These are the two deep sleep state conditions. We cannot go on sleeping for ever, nor should we wake up to misery. To combine the two, we must be conscious (awake) and we must also enjoy the homogeneity that is the characteristic of deep sleep. We must be awake and yet the ego-sense should not be awake; we must live and yet forget the world. The unalloyed happiness that we enjoy in deep sleep can be ours if we can forget ourselves during the waking state of activity – intense activity. Desires and cravings produce stress and tension, and it is only when these have been removed that we are really happy, for then we turn within ourselves. This does not last long. It is immediately followed by the rising of another craving and its chain reaction. This will go on till we (a) prevent the tension from building up, (b) stop the mind from craving for sense-gratification and (c) train the self to rest in the self all the time, enjoying perpetual happiness.

The dynamism which is part of our (and cosmic)

nature cannot be stamped out. But it is possible to let the ego-sense step down from the pedestal of sovereignty it has usurped and not to let desires and cravings, selfishness and self-aggrandisement, motivate actions. Then we live in a remarkable state in which the intellect is in a contemplative mood, while the body and mind are engaged in intense activity.

If we constantly think of and work for the welfare of all beings, self-forgetfully, we shall derive the same happiness that we had during deep sleep. It is strange that we fail to notice that when we are least conscious of our health, we are healthy; and when we are not mindful of pain, it disappears. When we run after the shadow of happiness, it runs away from us; it is because we push unhappiness away that it seems to lean so heavily on us.

The solution lies in rejoicing in the happiness of others and in understanding the magnitude of human suffering in this world. In both cases we forget the self; and that is the first condition for being happy.

Service. Serve all. Serve selflessly. Serve self-forgetfully and self-sacrificingly. This is the first principle of divine life, of yoga, of the contemplative dynamism of the Bhagavad Gītā.

5. ESSENTIALS OF SOCIAL SERVICE

"You cannot remain inactive even for a moment," says Lord Krishna in the Bhagavad Gītā. And the gospel of selfless social service of my master Swami Sivananada has this immutable law as its first corner-stone. Nature is ever active. We, too, are active by nature. That is the sign of 'life'.

Then, will it do if I am ever active, doing whatever I feel like in whatever manner I like doing it? The human being does not merely wish to live, to exist and to procreate, but to aspire to something nobler. That nobler mission is to serve all and to do good to all.

The world glorifies a philanthropist or a social worker, but it does not bother about his motives or about his inner nature. God is the inner ruler of man, the witness of our thoughts, feelings and motives. Swami Sivananda demands, "Scrutinise always your motives", for god looks to our motives more than to our spectacular deeds.

Action itself is inferior to the right attitude. Hence if we want to find our inner harmony, if we wish to commune with the inner reality, we should be good. If we are good in our very nature, we shall constantly and spontaneously do good, without the temptation of a reward or the incentive of self-aggrandisement.

Therefore Swami Sivananda declares: "Be good, do good – these four words constitute the fundamental essence of all religions, of the teachings of all the prophets of the world, of yoga and vendanta." This, then, is the second corner-stone of dedicated selfless social service.

Here is the third corner-stone. If we want to be happy and if we want to enjoy peace, we must transcend the ego-sense. In meditation, one transcends oneself and enjoys peace. In repeating or singing god's names, one transcends oneself and enjoys happiness. One cannot normally be engaged all the time in these practices. How, then, to live the normal life in this world and yet to be happy and peaceful? "Forget yourself in the service of humanity," says Swami Sivananda. He was himself the greatest exemplar of this doctrine. He was an embodiment of self-forgetful, selfless service.

"The wise man should do unattached what the ignorant man does with attachment," says the Bhagavad Gītā. The difference is not in the external form nor mode of life, but in the inner spirit of that life. Swami Sivananda taught us that it is the motive and the inner attitude that acts either as a bondage or a liberator.

The correct inner attitude is that of worship. This is the fourth and most important corner-stone of Gurudev's gospel of selfless (social) service. Performed in a spirit of worship of the omnipresent reality, our service and all our actions tend to liberate us, instead of binding us to the world and worldliness.

Two aspects of this divine worship are to be constantly borne in mind. They are (1) the whole world is a manifestation of the lord who receives the worship offered in the form of selfless service, and (2) we derive the power and the capacity to serve or to work from god who dwells within us. The first keeps us ever willing, ready and eager to serve and serve all, and render any service. The second keeps us away from the pitfall of egoism. We have to serve with intense zeal and yet remain unattached. We have to feel that the lord is working through us and yet be humble. We have to see the lord in all and yet sympathise with them.

If these fundamentals are clearly understood, we shall readily see the great qualities that go to make up the ideal social worker. Then service becomes yoga. It will not bind you, but liberate you.

6. THE POWER OF LOVE

Real service is very difficult to find these days. Work without our heart in it can build up tension within us and eventually lead to a nervous breakdown.

The man who learns to love his work, serves with love. He is ready and eager to pour every ounce of his energy into that service. He is not only free from tension, but he is full of joy, peace and satisfaction.

We are unhappy, not because someone is making us miserable, but because our heart has become so small that we want only our own happiness. Selfishness is an animal instinct. The extremely selfish man is an animal. The moderately selfish man is human. The truly unselfish man is a divine being. We live in order that we may reach that stage one day. To become divine is our goal. With god-given intelligence we can hasten our progress to this goal.

We saw that the first universal experience of happiness is deep sleep. There is another universal experience which goes unnoticed and unreflected upon. When are we intensely and consciously happy in our daily life? When we are close to one we love. If being near beloved ones makes us happy, it is simple logic that to be always happy we should always love all! If it is not possible to live always surrounded by our particular loved ones, then we should love all those who are around us at all times, and thus transform them into our 'beloved ones'.

Is it possible for you to love strangers? Yes, one of them is your wife now! Later others arrived, whom you had never seen before (total strangers) and these you call your children! There is a taint of selfishness in these relationships. That is why sooner or later they give us some amount of unhappiness. If these and all relationships cease to be commercial contracts and if love is pure and selfless, then we shall be always happy.

True unselfishness is not possible unless we recognise the hidden god in all. If you love your husband, your father, your mother, your child, or your friends, can you not see that you are in truth loving the omnipresence in and through every one of them? It is that omnipresence that stands in front of you as the wife, the son, the daughter, the friend. So, if you have learned to love this one person and if you can enter into the spirit of this experience of love, you realise: "This is the experience of love which delights my heart. In and through that person I am actually loving god, the omnipresence." Once you know what it is to love, expand that love, and let it cover more and more of the world in which you live.

This applies not only to the people with whom we associate, but also to the circumstances in which we are placed. Only man demands that god should adapt his gifts to man's wants, whereas animals accept god's gifts and adapt themselves to them. We must have full faith in god's goodness and learn to adapt, adjust and accommodate to whatever god gives us, in whatever condition or environment he places us.

God is our father-mother. It is the height of foolishness and ignorance to imagine he is going to punish us and send us terrible calamities and diseases. A bitter pill may be needed to correct an ailing body; and even the most loving mother will give it to her child. God is love. We must lovingly welcome whatever he gives us. And, we shall ever be happy. This is the attitude of a bhakta (devotee) who practises karma yoga.

7. *GOD IS LOVE*

God's blessings are showered equally upon all; but man is fond of depriving his neighbour of his share. Man has forgotten god. Therefore he has also forgotten that god is love. He has turned away from god in whose image he is made. Love is divine: hatred is diabolical. God is love. God is peace. God is bliss. If we wish to enjoy this peace we should grow in love. God has given man free-will to shape his own destiny. We should choose the path of love. Love should govern our thoughts, words and deeds.

God is the cosmic being. He cannot be enthroned in a heart which has shrunk through selfishness. It must expand, gradually, to include our neighbours, our community, and ultimately all beings in the universe. When this love is cultivated in our heart it will naturally express itself as service and charity. These will become part and parcel of our nature. Then we shall attain cosmic consciousness and enjoy supreme peace, eternal bliss and immortality. When the little 'I' (the selfish ego) dies, you will be god, full of love and compassion for all beings.

We cannot love one another truly unless we recognise that god who dwells in our heart dwells in the hearts of all. We cannot truly serve mankind and work for the good of all unless we feel that all of us together form the body of god. This knowledge and realisation should come first. Only then will political systems, economic theories and technological progress bear fruit.

It is dangerous to pay lip-homage to this doctrine. We should sincerely pray to him, meditate upon him every day. We should endeavour every moment of our life to express through loving service of our neighbour, the inner faith that god is omniprcsent. We should love all. It is then that we shall truly be human beings.

This is the essence of the teaching of all religions. This is yoga.

8. WISDOM LOOKS AT EVIL

What is the yogi's attitude towards evil?

Evil is primarily within us and it also exists in the objective universe as a neutral (tamasic – inert, ignorant and dark) factor. What we call 'evil' is for the most part a matter of opinion or tradition. For instance when you say A is wicked, there are others who say he is good. Drinking wine may be regarded as a great sin by the brahmin in India: but it is not so to a saintly man in France!

Secondly, evil is the projection of our own vanity, selfishness or ignorance on something outside. We find outside what we, within ourselves, want to find. If we are good and want only good, we shall find something good (god!) in the 'evil'. If we are evil, then we shall find faults even in god.

Thirdly, in god's own divine nature (which we call the manifest universe) we discover beings of different natures. One man is affectionate, another is harsh; but if you see the espression of love that is god in all these, your own heart will be filled with that love. Wind dries; water wets. Though of different or even opposite nature, they are all part of a single pattern – god's good world. They exist to serve him, his will and his purpose for the universe and all of us. The wise man understands them and benefits himself. The ignorant man interferes with them, to his own disadvantage.

Ignorance of this truth leads man to the violation of the divine law. Ignorance itself is sin, and this sin is followed by the necessary corrective measure, according to the divine law. Ignorance regards this corrective measure as pain! It rebels against it and commits more sins. The wheel of karma is kept revolving.

Wisdom consists of a threefold attitude to life: (a) evil is the dark side of nature, with its divine purpose of revealing and promoting goodness by contrast; (b) fault-finding, on the other hand, is the fruit of ignorance which nourishes, strengthens and perpetuates evil; and (c) pain, poverty, disease and the like are nature's measures to purify the inner nature so that the roots of sin (ignorance and craving) are removed and man's inner vision is turned to god.

Adoption of all three principles will at once give us peace and happiness. To condone evil in ourselves, condemn it in others and reject or run away from pain, is the very opposite of wisdom. Until we uncondition our inner being, we should be wary not to succumb to evil tendencies. Until we have purified our heart thoroughly, we should avoid evil company, too. That does not mean that we hate those whom we regard as wicked, nor should we take upon ourselves the duty of 'correcting' or 'reforming' others. In this we only succeed in adding to the evil in ourselves.

Remove the inner evil first. You will love all. And, that love will transform everyone you come into contact with.

9. A FORGOTTEN VITAL SECRET

Selfless service is its own 'achievement'. If one serves in order to gain something, the service is not 'selfless'. Motives are often hidden within the subconscious; it is not easy to detect them. You may 'give up' desire for material reward, but secretly wish to be admired. You may 'run away' from such admiration, but enjoy a 'spiritual satisfaction' within yourself. An honest appraisal of the situation must enable you to appreciate that the whole life is tainted with selfishness and as long as the mind functions and the ego-sense prevails, selfishness lurks in some corner of your personality. When this is clearly seen and when the danger of selfishness is realised at the same time, there is great vigilance, in which there is no selfishness. Such vigilance is meditation.

Otherwise service, though begun with pure love, often leads to the very results it is meant to avoid – either we get attached to the people we love and serve, or (if their response is inimical) we are angered, or we even dislike or hate them.

There is a mysterious power deep within us which does not allow us to love all and serve all. It generates two currents of attraction and repulsion, attachment and hatred, likes and dislikes. Helplessly we are drawn in different directions by these two currents and do not even make an attempt to free ourselves from them. Thus, never finding harmony within, never loving and serving selflessly, we live in total dissatisfaction and frustration – all because we are unable to free ourselves from likes and dislikes and dive deeper into our centre, beyond these.

Nothing but meditation (coupled with selfless service, which is dynamic meditation) can enable us to rise above these two currents of rāga (infatuation, attachment, desire) and dveṣa (hate, anger, aversion). Therefore our masters ask us to meditate daily. And if we are sincere in our approach to and practice of meditation we must arrive at the truth that the god who dwells in our heart dwells in all. This realisation must come, sooner or later; sooner, if at the same time we endeavour to practise selfless service of humanity and cultivate cosmic love. A very good exercise in meditation is to start with visualising an image of god in our heart: we have to fix the mind somewhere and the heart is the centre of our being. Let this image expand and enlarge, as you get nearer and nearer to god, so that eventually the original position is reversed: God is not part of me, but I am part of god. Even so, all are part of god. God is the cosmic being. We are all autonomous but interdependent cells in that body. Because we are autonomous we can love; we are not pre-destined to hate each other. We love one another, not for the sake of one another, but for the sake of the self that is all.

When this truth is actually realised then to love all and to serve all will be effortless, and we shall then have an entirely different attitude to the world. We will love god in all and serve him in all, not as a good policy, not for any gain, not as a privilege, nor even as a duty, but because it is quite natural and inevitable. And this love never wanes; for there is no selfish motive here to wane.

When we forget ourselves and the world, we enjoy peace and happiness, and we enjoy them consciously while we are engaged in our daily work. This is my master's divine message. This is the religion of tomorrow.

10. YOGA FOR INTEGRAL PERFECTION

Yoga or 'divine life' is divinising our entire life, all our activities. We cannot be saints for an hour of the day and sinners for the rest. Our masters, therefore, plead for integral perfection. They exhort us to combine all the spiritual practices in our daily life and thus ensure that we have a 'balanced spiritual diet' which enables us to grow harmoniously into a perfect personality. Theoretically, it is supposed to be sufficient to deal a fatal blow at the ego with the axe of the yoga that is suited to one's temperament. In practice we discover it is not so. Hence it is better to adopt a concerted attack.

Even the so-called different yogas or paths to god realisation are not really so different! Or exclusive! A close examination reveals that they are all interconnected. Activity (karma yoga) without love of the omnipresent god (bhakti yoga) and knowledge of the truth (jñāna yoga), or the latter without right activity, is nearly impossible.

They are inseparable and cannot be independently practised. The emphasis differs in accordance with the difference in individual temperament. If there is god at heart, his love must flow in and through all our limbs. If there is knowledge of god in the 'head', it must compel us to love him, too. Head, heart and hand must respond to god-love.

The Indian spiritual aspirant is an optimist. He knows that without purification he cannot get god-realisation. He knows that karma yoga which implies multiplicity (a finger cannot scratch itself), and bhakti yoga which implies duality, and jñāna (direct intuitive realisation of oneness) which asserts unity, are rationally incompatible, and yet he practises them together. He does not understand the Upaniṣhaḍs but reads them daily. When the heart is purified through karma yoga and the mind is steadied by bhakti-rāja-yoga, then the knowledge of the Upaniṣhaḍs illumines his soul.

Perfection is a synthesis of all yogas. Rāja yoga steadies the mind and jñāna yoga pours wisdom into it. Feeling is perfected by bhakti yoga. 'Living' is perfected by karma yoga. The instrument with which we are able to practise yoga, the body, is looked after by haṭha yoga. All these together constitute yoga. They are inseparable, even as the three faculties (thinking, feeling and 'living') are inseparable in us.

11. SELF DISCOVERY

In this self-development towards perfection, no-one can help you and no-one can hinder you either. There are two reasons. This perfection is already there, waiting to be discovered; and secondly, you are unique. No-one else has the exact replica of your personality.

A sculptor looking at a marble slab 'sees' the figure of Krishna or Christ in that slab. He does not add anything, it is there already. But there is a lot more marble, in addition to that figure. He merely removes the extraneous chips and what remains is what he saw in the slab in the first instant.

First you have to see this unique spirit that is built into you. When you do, you also see a lot of rubbish sticking to this central being. As you keep eliminating these (or 'this rubbish') the latent perfection is discovered and there is total development. In order to discover yourself you must not assume there is only goodness in you. You must also be aware of what is diabolical and devilish in you too. When you thus become aware of the divine and the diabolical in you simultaneously, you know what to do!

To ascribe the cause of an inner evil to something outside oneself is immature. If you cut your foot on the coral you immediately fix it. There is no time to blame anyone. You become one with the problem, the pain, and the pain demands immediate relief.

When you thus observe yourself inwardly, there is

utter stillness of mind. It is transparent, and in that transparent mind you can see the play of thoughts, you can be aware of the 'evil' in your personality.

You learn actively to watch the thoughts, without thinking those thoughts. When this watchfulness or awareness becomes constant and efficient, keen and sensitive, it detects an 'evil' thought even as it enters the field of consciousness; and keeps it away, because the evil thought hurts the inner being.

While cultivating this watchfulness or awareness, the question one asks concerning the thought is "What is this thought made of, and who thinks it?" and not "Why is it there?" If you ask the question in the right manner, you will known the answer, immediately and experientially, not verbally. The asking itself is the answer. The questioning is important, for it directs the attention to the very source of thought. When an undesired or evil thought arises from this source, this attention itself neutralises such thought.

In this self-enquiry, there are two delicate factors to be carefully and vigilantly borne in mind: there is unrelenting vigilance which burns steadily within you, reducing to ashes every 'evil' or undesired thought even as it rises, because such a thought hurts you; and when your mind becomes aware of similar evil outside, in others, you are extremely sympathetic, for you do not judge or condemn.

What is that state of perfection that this self-enquiry reveals, and what are its characteristics? The Bhagavad Gita provides an inspiring answer: perfection is that state in which all cravings end. It is there all the time. But you have turned away from it. When you turn away from the sun, you see the shadow; and the shadow has all the appearance of yourself. But when you wheel around and face the light, you see only the sun, the light and not yourself. That is god-realisation, self-realisation. That is perfection.

The whole process of yoga, of spiritual development, is the removal of obstacles to this realisation. In order to see these obstacles one needs a tremendously calm mind.

Quietness of the mind does not mean that there are no thoughts. There may be millions of waves on the surface of the ocean, but underneath it is absolutely calm. Can you go down to the depth of the 'ocean' within you, the depth of your own consciousness, so that even while the thoughts keep rising and falling on the surface, there is this deep calm and peace? This is the most important thing.

Disturbance in the mind goes on as long as you cling to false values, to any values at all. When you directly realise that nothing that the mind and the ego have cherished so far is of any value there is instant, complete and permanent cessation of disturbance; there is enlightenment.

12. PRACTISE YOGA AND LOVE IT!

Yoga is intelligent practice. Swami Sivananda asks us to reflect and analyse ourselves, to understand our capacities and limitations, our hidden potentialities and lurking weaknesses, and then to formulate a spiritual plan for self-discovery.

We know a lot, but do little. Idle knowledge is more dangerous than ignorance, for it adds to our vanity. If we know a little and put that into practice, we shall liberate ourselves. Even our self-analysis and its resultant estimation are validated only by their application in practice. Based on our understanding of our need, we ought to take a few resolves. These will assume the form of a determination to grow in virtue, to eradicate evil habits, to do a little of various spiritual practices like yogāsanas, breathing exercises, meditation, study, charity, worship, japa, kīrtan, selfless service and satsaṅga. Then we should draw up a daily routine incorporating all these in it. Even if we do a little of each item of yoga practice, if we are regular we can achieve a lot.

There is often a human tendency to make big resolutions, do something for a few days and then to let the zeal cool off. To prevent this our master gives us a priceless companion, the spiritual diary. In it we record to what extent we were able to carry out our resolutions and to what extent we neglected the daily routine.

Of course, none of those is meaningful if it is undertaken as a gimmick or in obedience to the dictates of someone else or as a proud record of one's spiritual progress. Genuine sincerity is needed for real, natural, unspectacular progress.

13. ARE WE SINCERE?

Only the insincere man grumbles and finds difficulties. If you have sincerity at heart there is no impossibility, and difficulties are accepted as necessary challenges. The sincere man converts obstacles into stepping stones. The insincere man regards stepping stones as obstacles. On the path of yoga, what is needed is sincerity, and if we are sincere and earnest, then the path is smooth. Sincerity itself is only the inner expression of the correct scale of values. We are sincerely devoted to only that which we value. Otherwise, we treat it as hard labour.

If you value anything, you want to do it and love doing it. If you do not value it, your mind magnifies only the difficulties involved.

As proof of sincerity the ancient masters looked for what are known as the 'four means of salvation' which every aspirant is encouraged to cultivate. These four means are: (1) discrimination (the recognition of the proper scale of values), (2) dispassion (its adoption to daily life), (3) virtues which induce one-pointed application of the mind and heart to the goal of life and (4) keen desire to attain that goal. These are fundamental to all our endeavours – sacred and secular – and cannot be dispensed with. Time does not efface nor alter these eternal verities. In order to be aware of these verities, one has to realise the futility of relying upon changing phenomena and fleeting objects of pleasure, upon the elusive inner emotions and divisive thought processes which perpetuate inner conflict and the consequent restlessness and unhappiness. Unless we realise the danger of relying on false values, we shall not seek true values.

One who has these four means takes to yoga as a duck takes to water. But one who neglects them regards spiritual life as a labour or burden to be carried. The secret of overcoming this unpleasantness lies in understanding the fact that we are bound to realise the self (god) one day or the other and it is a great joy doing so now; and also in taking a keen interest in boldly venturing into the realms of the mind and the spirit in full recognition of the truth that the 'other path' (the path of sense-pleasure) is worthless and is fraught with pain and sorrow. Then yoga becomes delightful and fruitful. Occasional setbacks lose their depressing effect, but act as stepping stones to greater effort and success.

14. YOUR NORMAL LIFE IS YOGA

If there is a change of heart and a change of values, then our daily life itself becomes divine life. 'Normally' we live in a fool's paradise with our scale of values tilted in favour of sense pleasures.

These evanescent objects of pleasure are often referred to as illusory; they are part of an illusion which is so, not because it does not exist at all, but because it appears to be what it is not. The world is not false but the 'world-appearance' is false. Matter exists: and both vedanta (Indian philosophy) and science agree that this matter itself is not what it appears to be, but a universal system of light-soundwaves (energy). But it is ignorant man who perceives in them, here an object of enjoyment which attracts him, and there a painful object which repels him.

Of this ignorance the first born is egoism (the feeling 'I am this') and the second offspring is selfishness (which manifests itself as desire and possessiveness – 'This is mine'). If a man is able to overcome these two by removing ignorance which enshrouds the soul, then his scale of values also changes, he perceives the reality of the universe. It then appears to him as it is; at present we see the world outside as we like or dislike – the world outside is but a projection of our own wishful thinking. A toy is a companion to a child, a marketable commodity to a businessman and a piece of delicate workmanship to an artist. It is an item of expenditure to the buyer and of income to the seller! These are relative, changeable values; but hidden within, there is a real value. What is it? That is what the yogi, the man of wisdom, asks himself all the time.

When these false values disappear, the world does not disappear too. A swimming pool does not become the Himalayas to a yogi or a sage. These remain as they truly are: not as they appear to be in the eyes of an ignorant man who perceives in them an object of pleasure or pain, profit or loss, good or evil. It is then that the animal instincts are sacrificed at the altar of truth, reality or god, and man shines as a real human being, the crown of god's creation, made in the image of god!

This is the object of creation and the purpose of human birth. But, this animal to be sacrificed is not outside us, but inside us. The world of matter includes our own body; and what applies to the objects of this world applies to our body – which is also perishable, etc. Therefore the yogi who knows that the objects of sense-pleasure are deceptive, also knows that his own senses which experience pleasure in them are also deceptive. It is only when we finally overcome even the sensations of pleasure and pain in us, that we are truly above the illusion of phenomena and close to the reality that is god.

To the yogi who has arrived at this sublime state of consciousness all life is sacred, all life is divine, all life is yoga. He lives in god, for god and as god, and he sees the whole universe (including his body) as the body of god; sees that it moves and lives according to his (god's) will. Such a life is called karma yoga.

Karma yoga is also a sādhanā (the means) to reach this sublime goal: and we shall discuss it in the next chapter.

☆ ☆ ☆ ☆ ☆ ☆ ☆ ☆ ☆ ☆

Chapter Two

KARMA YOGA

15. CONTEMPLATIVE DYNAMISM

Karma yoga plays a vital role in the total scheme of yoga practice. But, it is one of the most misunderstood of doctrines. All action is not yoga, though all action can be transmuted into yoga. The surgeon inserts a knife into someone's abdomen and a murderer does so too; but, what a difference! It is the difference that exists between a devout Hindu offering crumbs of bread to the fish in the holy river Ganga and the modern gentleman 'offering' to the fish a worm on a hook.

We have to understand the spirit of karma yoga thoroughly. For according to lord Krishna it is the spirit in which the action is done that matters, not so much the action itself–though the spirit always expresses itself in right action. If the right attitude is maintained and the correct spirit understood, then all action becomes yoga. If not, even great acts of charity and service, however good and beneficial they may be, do not constitute yoga. Doctors and nurses in hospitals, workers in charge of charitable institutions, priests and mendicants do not automatically attain salvation, unless the yogic attitude of humble workshipful service is present.

A poor man offering "a cup of water, a leaf, a flower or a fruit" with devotion to the lord-in-all, practises yoga; whereas, a millionaire donating a million rupees to an orphanage only pays indirectly the advertisement charges for his name and glory to be published in the newspapers!

What is the spirit of karma yoga? It is picturesquely

presented in the Bhagavad Gita:

"Man attains perfection by worshipping with every one of his actions the omnipresent God in whom all beings have their origin and in whom they exist."

(18-46)

This spirit of worship is most important. It presupposes the recognition of the hidden godhead in all. "God pervades all beings," says the Īśāvāsya Upanishad. "I am the self of all beings," says Lord Krishna in the Bhagavad Gita. It is only when we thus see and serve the lord in all, that we shall serve selflessly (without any selfish motive for gaining selfish ends), regarding the act or the service itself as reward enough. Only then shall we serve all with equal vision and balanced mind.

This is extremely difficult to understand, if we do not watch a living yogi demonstrate it. I have seen such a demonstration times without number in the life of my master Swami Sivananda. In fact, his divine life was one continuous commentary on the verse of the Gita cited above. After serving you he always thanked you for the opportunity that you, his god, gave him for thus worshipping the lord in you. In rendering this service no consideration of caste, religion, nationality, etc., ever swayed him. For all the time the master was conscious that the lord was hidden in the person whom he served and the service was worship of the divine. When he was serving the sick as a doctor in Malaya, before he renounced the world in 1923, he shared whatever he had with the patients, whatever their caste or social status. He did not charge them any fees, but gave them some pocket money when they departed, to help them buy their food.

It is in that spirit that we should work, in order to transform all our activities into yoga. Then would we live a life of meditation, constantly remembering the lord and yet doing our duty in this world. That is contemplative dynamism, karma yoga, the yoga of the Bhagavad Gita – the yoga for you.

16. NOT I, BUT THE LORD

The most important factor which transforms all activity (and so life) itself into yoga, is the inner understanding and knowledge that we are not serving humanity, but god in all. The next important factor in the 'nimiṭṭa bhāvanā', the attitude born of the realisation that 'god himself is serving his own manifestations through us and we are but instruments in his hands'. A moment's reflection will convince us beyond doubt that some mysterious power functions through us and enables us to serve and even to live. If that is withdrawn or even modified, a wise man may become stupid and an intelligent man may become insane. If that is withdrawn, all our virtues and wisdom lose their lustre. If that is withdrawn, the body turns into a corpse and it is immediately disposed of. It is because of the presence of that spark of god or image of god in us that we are considered human beings.

The karma yogi does not forget this great truth even for a moment. "Na ahaṁ kartā iśvaraḥ kartā" (I am not the doer, but the lord is the doer) is his constant feeling. He reminds himself often of the emphatic declaration of lord Krishna in the Bhagavad Gita (addressing Arjuna): "Even if you did not do your duty, fight this battle and kill these unrighteous people, they will not live. I have done away with them already; be a mere instrument in my hands." If we bear this in mind constantly, we shall not even claim any special merits for being good or doing good; it is he that is good in us and it is he that does good through us. No special reward is necessary: and if there is to be any special reward, it belongs to him!

This understanding or realisation may develop in three stages:

(1) We see what we do as duty. "This is my duty, I am discharging my duty." If you observe yourself very carefully at this stage, you see that there is some sourness in this attitude! The duty seems to bind us, not free us and liberate us – it seems to hold us in check, to constrict us. Yet, it may be necessary for the baby-soul. That is where we start. The rod of duty knocks down all your desires of profit motive and so on.

(2) You begin to wonder: "What is duty?" If a mosquito bites the back of my neck, is it the duty of my hand to chase it away? Oh, no. The hand does not argue, it does not say, "It is my duty to go and help my brother neck". Because the two belong to the same organism, there is spontaneous activity. There one discovers love. It is not duty but it is done out of love. We serve one another because we are linked by a central essence – truth, reality, god or self. We all form part of one god and therefore serve one another.

(3) In these two attitudes there is still a feeling of 'I' and 'another'. First you do it as a duty and then you do it because you love all. In the third and the last stage, the question "Why do I do this?" does not arise. The action is done – only actions exist. Neither the actor nor the person to whom the action is directed – only actions exist. We are all cells in the cosmic body of god; there is no 'I' here, nor a 'you' there. There is only one body of god. That is the reality, the rest is only a veil. When the 'I' and the 'you' have both been absorbed in the truth of god, what remains is pure action – which has been described and interpreted and misinterpreted.

"Be an instrument in my hands," Krishna tells Arjuna, his disciple. But as you meditate on this concept of an instrument you realise something marvellous. You take a pen in your hand and write – the pen is an instrument in your hand. You think, "Ah, I have understood. I am an instrument in the hand of god, like this, and I do his will." Look at the pen again. Does it know it is an instrument in your hand? No. Even that idea of being an instrument is not there; even the instrument-feeling is an egoistic notion, a manifestation of your own separate ego-sense. So even that is dropped.

When you lift the pen again, you see that all that happens is that the pen writes. The pen does its job, without thinking that it is its duty. There is neither the doer nor the object to which the deed is directed, but there is pure action.

When we can reach this stage of pure action, non-volitional action, instantly all problems disappear, because the creator of the problem, the ego, has been discovered to be non-existent. The body-mind complex is the channel for the flow of divine energy; that is, the egoless person has no 'I' but is a body-mind complex. This is what is referred to as 'god's will'. It only means 'I' is not the doer.

God's will alone prevails here; and we are able to live, to love and to serve by his will and power only. To surrender our little will and merge it in his is a great blessing; it liberates us from selfishness and egoism. Only he who has clearly grasped this spirit, and lives in that spirit, is and can be truly humble. The man who tries to cultivate 'humility' as a virtue in itself often lands himself in the 'arrogance of humility' or 'pride of humility'. But he who has understood that god does everything here and that we are all but his instruments or cells in his cosmic body, is truly humble. Let no action spring from your own private intentions, and you will instantly be freed from self-willed, egoistic, selfish activity and the consequent worries and anxieties.

An instrument has no anxiety to do! Why is it then that in our heart there is such a tremendous anxiety to be an instrument in the hands of god? That anxiety is the surest sign that the ego is very much anti-god. It thinks 'without me, god cannot function'. So the important thing is to *be.* In order to be, you do not have to try to be. Either you are or you are not doing the lord's will. Your only job is to look cautiously and constantly within at the springs of your own actions.

This, too, was readily evident in the daily life of our master Swami Sivananda. His genuine humility, his total unselfishness, and his wonderful optimism even in the face of seeming crisis in the life of the institution he had so painstakingly built up, were the surest indications of the total self-surrender to the divine will in which he worked. Never once did the master look back with satisfaction or pride on his own superhuman achievements, not did he ever rest on his laurels.

I have never seen another person who lived more truly in the eternal present, ever looking forward to doing more and more in the service of humanity, as the worship of the lord. He exalted dynamic selfless service as the best form of meditation and worship of the lord, though he always advised us to combine both service and meditation in order to evolve the synthesis of 'contemplative dynamism', karma yoga.

The karma yogi lives in two worlds at the same time. He works in the external world, but never loses sight of the inner world. He serves humanity, but is ever conscious that he is serving god. He works with his body and mind, but never forgets that they are instruments in the hands of god, the indweller. To guard against the selfish nature, he adopts the Nārāyāna-bhāvana (I am serving god in all) and to guard against the lower human, egoistic nature, he adopts the nimiṭṭa bhavana (not I, but god). When vanity is removed, all the evils in one's own personality are removed; all our evils spring from vanity. Vanity confuses the distinction between right and wrong: so, once vanity is removed, right action becomes spontaneous. Nimiṭṭa Bhavana fills us with inexhaustible power and energy. We do his work; in fact, he does his work, using us as instruments. He is omnipotent and so his instruments, too, enjoy abundant energy.

The spirit of karma yoga frees us from another problem in our daily life, the shock from which we suffer when someone whom we have served and loved is rude to us, insults us or hurts us. We do not resent when someone repays a debt he owes in any coin; we are happy. When that repayment takes the form of an insult or injury, why should we react differently? In fact, why should we react at all? Let others react as they will; we shall do what we should. And if our nature is divine and loving, our actions (even those which appear to be reactions) will always be divine and loving. Happy in all conditions let us continue to serve all selflessly, self-sacrificingly and untiringly, feeling that we are serving the lord in all for his sake, as his instruments.

That is the secret of karma yoga which liberates us from saṁsāra (birth and death) with the help of the very activities which otherwise bind us to this wheel of birth and death.

17. RELIGION FOR THE MODERN MAN

The entire universe is ever active. Man shares this nature, too. The Bhagavad Gītā says that no one can remain inactive even for a moment. The doctrine that to act in this world was to invite reaction – the chain that binds us to the wheel of repeated birth and death – involved a gross self-deception, because the very expression 'to do nothing' is absurd and meaningless. The man who 'sits doing nothing' is doing something – sitting! It is impossible to 'do nothing'. You are breathing, you are thinking, you are living. The Bhagavad Gītā calls him a hypocrite who sits as if doing nothing but who lets his mind think of ever so many objects. His physical organs may not be experiencing them, but his inner senses are, and his mind most certainly creates its own field of enjoyment and satisfies itself. That man is a lazy hypocrite, deceiving himself and perhaps others, too.

Hence it is that our master Swami Sivananda calls upon everyone, even the recluse, to come out into the world and to be dynamic in service – but with a difference.

The service should be selfless. This is the religion we need today – the religion of selflessness, of unselfish and loving service. We are all brothers and sisters. The entire world (not only the human kind, but all living beings) forms one family. Our physical body is made of 'earth' and when we leave it, it is returned to the earth. Earth is our mother who gave us birth and who nourishes us. 'Dust thou art and to dust returnest', was not said of the soul of man. Perhaps the *soul* is the individual *cell* in the body of god. God is our father; earth is our mother. We are all the children of this divine couple. What they give us belongs to everyone of us. Whatever be our status, knowledge or prowess, we have no right to deprive our brother of his share of our parent's blessings. The sense of possession should therefore go, because it is false and meaningless.

A gentleman was bathing in a river. A good walking-stick floated along the current. The gentleman caught hold of it; there was no one else to claim it. As he was heading for the bank, the cloth he had wrapped around his waist began to slip. When he held the cloth the walking-stick slipped from his hand and was carried away by the current. He beat his face and cried aloud: "Oh, my walking-stick has gone." Isn't it strange that holding it in his hand for a few seconds should bestow this ownership on him?

That is what we do with the goods of this world. They belong to the earth, to all of us. We should learn to share them with all. We should learn to give, give and give. This is my divine master's forte. I have not seen anyone else in the world take such an actual delight in giving, giving – everything to everybody.

A correct understanding of this truth that the world belongs to all of us and that we are all brothers and sisters under the fatherhood of god, will show us how we can achieve perfect social adjustment here. For, whatever may be our concept of god (they are but concepts which do not always have relevance to our life here) unless and until we truly understand our relationship with the world, we cannot know how to live in harmony with what is around us; we cannot attain purity of mind and heart and we cannot arrive at the truth.

Our relationship with our neighbours now is not governed by the universal teaching, 'Love thy neighbour as thyself', but by the profit motive. We have not learnt to give, but only to take — and there is no limit to what we want to take. Even if the whole world is given to us, we still remain unsatisfied. We expect to be paid for every little service we render. This expectation always brings disappointment in its wake. We are not interested in others' welfare, but only in our own.

Yoga asks us to serve and love our neighbour as our own self, for god's sake. "For god's sake, do this," cries a boss when he is annoyed; the wise secretary should thank him for this great admonition. We should do our duty for god's sake, not for the sake of pleasing any person.

We shall never feel disappointed if we expect no material reward for the service we render. We feel that the self that dwells in us dwells in all, and that we are eternally united with all that exists in a bond of love – and that love is god. In order to attain cosmic consciousness we cultivate cosmic love and express it as selfless service for god's sake, as an instrument in the hand of god.

Let not the thought enter our mind that we have brought any great good, happiness or relief to any being on earth. It is not that but for us, the world will collapse! God's will is done here, as it is in heaven. We are only his instrument. How blessed it is to be an instrument in the hands of god, to feel that his will is done through us. He works through us. His will is done and we are glorified on earth. Unearned glory!

In this there is no superior service or inferior service, no menial service and no service from which we need shrink. It is all service of god. Whatever falls to our lot we should do in this spirit. It is not necessary for us to run away from our homes and search for sick people! Wherever we are we shall find poor people, sick people, illiterate people, people in distress, etc., whom we can help. But over and above all this, we should learn to do all our daily duties – even the prosaic household duties and office work – in this spirit.

This spirit of worship ensures that the service or the activity is sincere and efficiently performed. We shall not offer faded flowers at the feet of god. We shall not be inefficient in our work either. We do not seek a reward: to worship him, to be an instrument in his hands, is itself the supreme reward. There is no mechanical regimentation in this work. It is full of love and devotion. It is performed joyously – there is no tension in such activity.

This is the religion for the modern man. It is the religion of transformation of the heart, a new social adjustment, a healthier outlook on life and one that satisfies the dynamic, rational and socialistic modern man. Everyone living for 'others' promotes commonweal and eventually realises the supreme omnipresent truth, or cosmic consciousness.

When this spirit is absent, commonweal, peace, happiness and prosperity are beyond our reach, whatever be the progress we make in the spheres of science and technology.

18. THREE-PRONGED ATTACK ON IGNORANCE

In karma yoga (and in yoga, generally) we have only one real enemy and obstacle and that is egoism: and this egoism itself is nothing but ignorance. This mighty power manifests in our life as (a) I-ness (b) mine-ness and (c) love of sense-pleasure and comfort. The purpose of yoga is specifically to forget the self, the ego, to forget the world of pleasure and comfort that is likely to keep one away from god – god who is present in all, and who is bliss.

This ignorance manifests itself as the basic concept: 'I am this body', i.e., I am a distinct personality, different from all others, with my own soul separate from others, with my own ideas, ideals, thoughts and aspirations. The yogi endeavours to 'sacrifice' (in the Bhagavad Gītā this is called yajña) this ignorance at the altar of god who is the sole reality.

This ignorance manifests as a distinction between what is 'mine' and what is 'not mine'. If this is an object of enjoyment there arises a tendency to preserve what is 'mine' with all one's power and by all means, fair and foul; and what is 'not mine' is sought to be gained, by fair means or foul. If it is a person, then the tendency is to cling to and to protect what is 'mine' and to ignore, to hate and even to destroy what is 'not mine'. The destruction of what is 'mine' causes misery; and the promotion and prosperity of what is 'not mine' also causes misery – whereas the contrary gives pleasure. The yogi endeavours to rid himself of this manifestation of ignorance by what in the Bhagavad Gītā is called 'dāna' (charity).

On account of the identification of the self with the perishable, inert and element-compounded body, this ignorance considers those experiences which please the senses, as happiness of the self! Hence, man restlessly pursues sense-pleasure, forgetting that thereby he is driving happiness farther away! Ignorance prevents him from arriving at a correct understanding and keeps him under the subjection of illusion. The yogi conquers this 'love and pursuit of pleasure' by resolutely leading a life of simplicity (austerity or tapas) which burns the veil of ignorance.

All three terms have been grossly misunderstood. Let

us approach the three from the lower end of the scale, for without first getting rid of the false values in our life and of the lust for luxury, we shall not get anywhere. Tapas is a 'burning fire', often taken literally to mean that we should live surrounded by fire! There are yogis in India even today who sit on burning sands of a river-bed with the blazing mid-summer sun above and four heaps of burning firewood in the four directions close to them. It may develop one's power of endurance, but it has no real spiritual value – for, instead of burning ignorance and its offspring (egoism) such practices may very well fatten egoism and vanity. A simple life, providing oneself with nothing more than the bare necessities of life (not those luxuries which today have become bare necessities), a life of self-control, is tapas; for such a life burns all unholy appetites of the senses.

Charity has also been distorted very much. Real charity is done, not because otherwise human misery will not be relieved (god can wipe out the world's miseries in a minute but he gives us an opportunity to purify our own heart by charity and service), not for the sake of self-aggrandisement, but purely as worship of the omnipresent god. We offer to the god-in-the-beneficiary that which already belongs to him. The whole universe is his, and we ignorantly feel that some objects are 'mine'. Charity is done in order to remove this sinful feeling of mine-ness, this anti-divine misappropriation which is the cause of all our miseries.

Yajñā or sacrifice, too, has given rise to hideous practices of killing innocent and harmless animals in the name of god and religion. Sacrifice is the sacrifice of egoism, selfishness, which erects a wall of isolation to imprison the soul. This is the last big hurdle in yoga; and just beyond it is god-realisation. This selfishness is the poisonous agent that pollutes the living waters of peace and bliss that continuously spring from our own heart, thus making us miserable even though we live close to the fountain-source of supreme happiness and peace. Sacrifice of I-ness is not easy: it is not giving away something which we have (and which we may acquire again!), but is the little ego which we, in ignorance, believe to be the self. When this ego-sense dies, then the cosmic being reveals itself from within as the self.

These three are vital to the practice of yoga. Tapas simplifies our life and makes luxuries unnecessary. It opens our eyes to all the unnecessary things we store in our own house, which when distributed can lessen our anxiety over their preservation and promote the happiness of others. Charity removes the sense of possession and enables us to realise that all things belong to god and are really pervaded by him. Sacrifice removes the veil of ignorance and egoism in us and enables us to perceive the hidden godhead within.

Sacrifice and charity together keep us ever open in all the aspects of our personality. Self-centredness and selfishness are destroyed and we are ever open to the reception of divine light and to its rediffusion to all.

☆☆☆☆☆☆☆☆☆☆

Chapter Three

BHAKTI YOGA

19. LOVE OF GOD AND MAN

We studied karma yoga, the yoga of dynamic selfless service or what I have called 'contemplative dynamism' at some length, for the simple but important reason that it is the best approach suited to the present age. For, partly on account of the total extroversion of man's consciousness and partly as a reaction to the idle pretenders of holiness living a parasitic life, there is a world-wide revolt against life-and-world-negating forms of asceticism and cloistered mystery. Whilst all the masters of divine wisdom (from lord Buddha, lord Jesus, prophet Muhammed and lord Krishna down to our own masters in the present age) have acclaimed with one voice that we should love god with all our heart and soul, they have almost equated this love with the love of man. One without the other is incomplete. Love of god without the love of man may amount to deception. Love of man without love of god may lead to worldliness and bondage, however well-meant it is. We need an integration of the two: and that is yoga.

In fact, that is what we learn from the christian symbol of the holy cross. It represents the message of yoga and the vital teachings of lord Jesus and lord Krishna. Almost all the major religions of the world have symbols to embody this truth.

I look at the two arms of the holy cross – the vertical and the horizontal. The vertical arm seems to say to me: "O man! Love thy god with all thy being". The two ends of this vertical arm point one above and the other below. In other words god is above, far beyond the reach of your mind and intellect (transcendental) and he is below, in the innermost core of your being in the depth of your own heart.

I look at the horizontal arm of the holy cross. The outstretched arms of lord Jesus command me: "Love thy neighbour as thyself". Lord Jesus himself clearly stated who that neighbour is in the parable of the good samaritan. Here, it is good to remember that this horizontal arm points both to the right and to the left. In other words: "Love thy neighbour who is on your right (whom you regard as *righteous* and lovable), and also the neighbour whom you have *left* behind you (regarding him as wicked, uncivilised, undesirable and therefore your enemy) as your own self."

These two are not isolated and distinct activities. The two arms of the holy cross are joined together to indicate that the two aspects are in fact one: for, god dwells in your neighbour, and your love of your neighbour is 'not indeed for the sake of your neighbour, but for the sake of the self in him' (in the words of sage Yājñavalkya in the Bṛhadāraṇyaka Upanishad). The one god appears before us in these four directions: (a) above, as the transcendental reality, (b) below as the immanent reality in our own heart, (c) all that is good and glorious in this world, and (d) all that we, in our state of ignorance, have come to regard as evil and undesirable. Perhaps, it is in order to further underline and emphasise the last aspect that lord Jesus specifically added: "Love thine enemy"!

All saints and prophets have exalted love above all other virtues. They have at the same time warned us that that love should be pure and divine. That is, the love should not be directed towards the personality of the neighbour, but to the deeper inner reality – viz., god. Thus love of god must flow through our limbs as love of man, and that love of man is for the sake of the omnipresent being, god. You will love all – and not love some and hate others – only if you see the common unity in all. That is god.

It is easy to see, therefore, that karma yoga does not and cannot stand independent of other branches of yoga. It should either be based on the knowledge: "All activities spring from god's nature and not from me" – or on love of god: "I, an instrument in the hands of god, serve god in my neighbour, for god's sake." The former knowledge-approach (jṅāna yoga) is rare nowadays. The latter is within our reach. But it has its own discipline.

20. THE YOGA OF DEVOTION

We have seen how love of god and love of man are identical, two sides of the same coin. One without the other is sham and nonsense. This is very important to bear in mind. In loving man, we should not forget the god in him. In loving god, we should not forget that he is in all!

That is the wonderful message that lord Krishna has for us in the Bhagavad Gita. He asks us to think of god constantly and be united with him constantly; but never to neglect our duty! When we are puzzled if this is possible, he turns round and points out to us that he is in all. It is possible to love and serve him in all. It should be practised; but let us not minimise its difficulty, either.

He who does not know what it is to love one, does not know how to love any. He who has not felt the presence of god at all . . . how do you expect him to feel the presence of god in all?

To solve this problem, our ancients instituted the devotional practices, together called 'bhakti' in sanskrit. Bhakti means 'to resort to', 'to go to', 'to surrender oneself to', 'to take refuge in'. Please bear this in mind and you will realise how wrong it is to take this wonderful yoga to mean mere emotionalism. Yet, that is what has happened. Crying, jumping, dancing, fainting and such other abnormal practices have often been mistaken for true emotion, but all emotion is not devotion.

We often forget that though sages may behave like mad men, mad men are not sages. We should know the genuine from the spurious. Otherwise, we shall regard bhakti as a mere riot of emotion. It is not. Such a misunderstanding also provides a safe cover for all sorts of misdemeanour and undesirable behaviour.

We should take refuge in god. We should constantly go to god. We should constantly feel his presence (which is the same as his omnipresence). But, if we have never been in love, if we have never felt that presence in someone, something, somewhere, how shall we experience it in all?

Compassionate sages have provided us with a ladder with convenient rungs with easy steps to god-realisation. These are worship of an image of god in a specially erected holy place, singing of hymns, repetition of the divine name, etc. All these external 'aids' provoke the inner feelings of the presence of god which is most important. They all have their place in our approach to god. We use them as a child uses a doll (though there is a vital difference). The doll is not a baby; but the girl learns how to hold a baby. It is a vital part of training for eventual motherhood.

The child does not 'imagine' that the doll is a doll – you have seen how it is heartbroken when something happens to her 'child'. In all our spiritual devotional practices, it is good to bear this great factor in mind. We shall not forget that the goal is realisation, not imagination. We should see 'god' in the image. However, we have been conditioned to reject as superstition that which offends our rational intellect! In our devotional practice, therefore, we resort to imagination which the rational intellect accepts as a necessary focal point. In the practice of yoga, this imagination is soon substituted by 'visualisation'. Behind all forms is the formless. In every atom of matter is the spirit. The doll can never become a baby; the baby is not in it at all. But god's presence is omnipresent. That is the difference. The image does not 'contain' god, but is part of his omnipresence, anyway. To limit him is sin, blasphemy, spiritual tragedy (we shall not call a pot of ocean-water the 'ocean'); but to approach him through the image, because of our subjective limitation, is sensible. Knowing that air is universal, we do not demand that we shall only breathe the whole air or nothing, but sensibly breathe in a little, still asserting "I am breathing air".

God, being infinite, is all. God being the centre of everyone (which fact is symbolically expressed as 'God dwells in the hearts of all') is close to everyone and can be approached in infinite ways. The centre is equi-distant from every point on the circumference. Every man thus has direct and independent access to god. Hence, proselytisation is ignorant, if not disastrous.

The Bhagavad Gītā bestows on us (a) total freedom of worship, and (b) freedom from interference. A man-of-god proclaims the dangers of disturbing the faith on which a man's life is based and merely reveals the centre; and in the light of his teaching every man sees his own path and marches on it. If the blessings of god, (viz., sunlight, rain, air, food and life) are bestowed by him on all, who are we to say that unless they followed 'me', they will all go to hell? It is the worst blasphemy.

Even in regard to the individual's adoration of the one god, he is given total freedom of choice as to the form and the mode. The Bhagavad Gītā specifically mentions this. The hindu has taken advantage of this freedom and provided the devotee with innumerable 'images' of god. These act as (a) a focal point for the devotee's concentration and meditation; (b) a kind of shorthand for sublime philosophical concepts, and an unchanging pictorial language in which they are preserved; and (c) a consoling presence to which the devotee could resort in times of stress, trials and tribulations.

Of all spiritual practices, bhakti or devotion or love of god is one which involves the greatest amount of symbolism. The symbolism is not to be intellectualised but realised. First comes faith which generates love: love slips past the intellect and throws open the heart's doors and hence there is intuitive realisation of the symbolism. It is not an understanding of the symbolism, nor its rationalisation; but actualisation, revelation.

21. FROM RITUAL TO REALISATION

Bhakti yoga or love of god is basic to all religions that encourage their adherents to use icons and rituals in their spiritual practices. It is one of the main features of the Indian approach to god. This was regarded by ancient spiritual teachers as so vital that they wove it into the fabric of the Indian's daily life. In addition to a temple which is found in every village, every house has its own altar at which full-scale ritualistic worship is offered every day.

It is unfortunate that the common man clings to the icon and the ritual and forgets the spirit underlying their use. Worship of god-in-the-idol degenerates into idolatry which has nothing to do with religion but which is just another trade. However, whenever this has happened in India, it has immediately been arrested by saintly religious reformers who have restored to religion its pristine purity.

Man swings from one extreme to the other! People misinterpret the reformers' utterances and use them to their own advantage. The words of lord Krishna, the biblical prophets, lord Jesus, lord Buddha and prophet Muhammed sprang from their realisation or direct experience. It is good to hold them as 'lamps unto our feet' in order that we, too, may reach that experience. But when we assume the role of their representatives here and quote their words in order to run the followers of the other faiths down, then we present a grotesque picture thus described by a Tamil poet: 'An ugly bird saw a peacock dance; and, feeling equally important, spread its own plumes and began to dance!" The mischief is completed by the atheistic, materialistic and worldly man who uses all this to shake the faith of the devout.

We go to a temple, synagogue, church or mosque not in obedience to what the priest says, but to commune with god. We should not stop going there on account of what the priest says within it, nor what the reformer says outside it. To judge god and to make our devotion to him dependent on the thoughts, words, deeds of any man, is to blaspheme against god – you are the loser.

Understood and applied rightly, idol worship gradually leads the devotee to the realisation of the absolute. My master, Swami Sivananda, was devoted to idol worship till the end of his life, though he was a monistic philosopher. He was regular in his daily ritualistic worship of his deity. Thus he set an example for all of us to emulate. But he, as lord Krishna before him, reminded us that we should not stop there. We should practise constant remembrance of god. We should feel his (omni) presence everywhere, in all.

It is easy to say so, but quite another thing to do so. Two factors are involved in this: (a) we should know what it is to feel the presence of god – a 'salesman's sample' of it: and (b) we should have a method by which we can remember him.

The first is provided by the ritual of idol worship. The icon enables us to feel his presence and at the same time to look within and sample the feeling. Without it, it is possible that the novitiate may never experience the wonderful feeling of god's omnipresence.

The second is provided in the Bhagavad Gītā, the tenth chapter. The technique is this: let everything that we see remind us of god – the light of the sun, moon, stars, fire and the electric lamp; the vast blue sky or the ocean; the beautiful flower and the innocent face of a child; the gigantic tree and the strong arm of a gymnast; the image of god on the altar and the radiant face of a saint. All these remind us of the existence of god in them. Our master wanted us to practise constant nāma-smaraṇ (repetition of a mantra or the name of god). One helps the other. When they are combined, we grow god-conscious rapidly.

How does idol worship fit into this? What is an idol but a piece of matter, from the point of view of an ignorant man – whatever may be his wealth, position or titles? Yet, the devotee feels the presence of god within that material substance (clay, stone, metal or wood). The wise sage allows him to 'play' (pray) with it as a child plays with a doll. The child gets its training in mothercraft; the devotee gets to know that god indeed does dwell within that piece of matter. Then he turns around and sees the sun, moon, etc., and realises that even as god is the indweller of the idol, he is the indweller of the sun, moon, etc. This looks apparently simple, but in practice it is difficult.

Why does not the sage advocate such a practice of the presence of god, without prescribing idol worship as a preliminary? For the simple reason that the human mind is more ready to associate divinity with the idol (on account of tradition) than to see god in the face of a child. In the case of the latter, immediately your eyes behold it your mind says, "It is my child, etc.," and you have to overcome a good deal of thoughts and counter-thoughts before arriving at the ideal thought, "God is shining through its eyes". But, in the case of an idol this difficulty does not arise, on account of the age-old association of ideas. And, with a little practise, it becomes easy to extend the practice of the presence of god to everything in this world.

There is another important angle to this spiritual exercise. Idol worship should lead us on to meditation on the absolute. Without the first step of idol worship, meditation on the absolute is almost impossible, and if we do not extend the frontiers of divinity beyond the idol, we may get stuck there. Hence, even in the method of worshipping idols, our ancient seers introduced elements of adoration of the nameless and the formless being – in fact, they emphasised that we should superimpose the qualities of the absolute on the idol. In the mantras they provide for the worship, they wove expressions like "I bow to the all-pervading", "I bow to the eternal", which are obviously irrelevant to the personalised forms of god (e.g. Rāma and Krishna, who are historical personalities) which the devotee worships. Again, they declare that mental worship of the chosen deity is superior (when we are ready for it, of course!) to gross external worship, and that para pūjā (a way of adoring the omnipresent god through all our thoughts, words and deeds) is superior to all other forms of worship.

The sincere spiritual aspirant realises that he cannot get anywhere on this path without the help of an image to fix his mind on. The idol provides a concrete form of god on which he can pour out the devotion of his heart, to which he can pray, and on which he can lean in times of stress and strain, trials and difficulties. He finds great relief from tension, worries and anxieties when he has a 'tangible god' to whom he can talk! The omnipresent divinity, which is of course present in the idol too, hears his prayers.

When the concentration (which is love) grows intense, the power latent in the idol is revealed: and thus we have stories of the great mystics who could 'see' god in and through the idols. Let us not forget that god who is omnipresent is in the idol, too; and he who is omnipotent can reveal himself in any form to the devotee. It is in this respect that the idol is different from the child's doll. Whereas the doll remains forever a doll (because it is lifeless), the idol reveals the hidden godhead in response to the devotee's loving prayer and concentration. The concentrated beam of the devotee's consciousness will one day be powerful enough to burn the gross matter of the idol and liberate and reveal the hidden god in it; even as the rays of sunlight when focussed through a lens are able to burn a piece of cotton and make it burst into flame. But, let us not forget that it was not the idol that they saw in the vision, but the divinity in the idol – the divinity that is in all, for that matter. When asked if he saw the goddess Kāli with 'physical' eyes, Śrī Ramakrishna Paramahamsa explained that "God cannot be seen with these physical eyes. In the course of spiritual discipline one gets a 'love body' endowed with 'love eyes', 'love ears', and so on. One sees god with those 'love eyes' ".

Without correctly understanding this principle, people unwisely shout: "We do not want to worship a stone". Of course, they should not. But first answer these questions: "Who is worshipping the stone?" "I." "What idea have you of this 'I'?" The first one is of the body. It is the body that actually performs the worship. The body is predominantly water, with some other chemical elements. What harm is there in water and matter worshipping a stone? How is it ignorance or superstition? "Of course", you exclaim, "I am not only the body, but I have a soul." Then let the body worship the stone, let the heart, mind and soul in you realise the lord in the stone.

Secondly, will you worship all stones? No. Only a particular stone which has been given a shape. Who worships it? I. If this 'I' is also chiselled and sculptured into a divine shape, it is divine. The stone-image of god reminds you of this. When this was stone, you stood upon it. When those chips of the stone which did not belong to this divine form were chiselled away and the stone assumed the divine form, you worship it. In the same way, there is a lot of undivine element in you. Chisel it away. You will become a divinity on earth, adored by mankind. That, incidently, is the argument underlying the adoration of the guru or the spiritual preceptor.

If idol worship thus leads us step by step to god-realisation through the worshipful service and recognition of the omnipresence of god, it is ideal worship. Else, it degenerates into idle worship.

22. *CONQUEST OF THE CONQUEROR*

As we have seen, it is the concentrated mind that is able to pierce 'matter' and perceive the spirit. Its dissipated rays are powerless. We do have periods of one-pointed mind, but they are determined by external forces. For instance, when we are witnessing an exciting movie film, the mind seems to be one-pointed; but then it is not in our control and it is extrovert. On the other hand, when we wish deliberately to control it, it is more restless than the wind.

The mind moving with the speed and power of the wind itself is the conqueror of the whole world. Everything in this world has been achieved by the mind. Every great action and achievement in this world has had the mind (thought) behind it. Mind has conquered matter; mind governs matter. Who is to conquer the conqueror? The yogis have a simple answer: japa (repetition of a mantra or name of god). (Unfortunately in this world of complexities, the very simplicity of the answer makes people disbelieve in it.) In all our spiritual practices, japa plays a vital role. This was our master's forte. It is a solution to all our problems. It does not merely solve the problems, it dissolves the creator of problems, viz., the mind! All our problems are created by the impure mind. Repetition of a mantra is the best purifier of the mind and tranquillizer, too. The effect is best illustrated in the following story:

A yogi spent some time in the house of a devotee, and the young son of the poor family served him devotedly. While departing from the place, the yogi volunteered to fulfill any of the boy's wishes, as he had control over an invisible spirit. The boy, however, wanted the spirit to be loaned to him for some time, as he had many 'wants'. Relunctantly, the yogi gave the young man command over the spirit with the warning that if he found any difficulty in dealing with it, he should think of the yogi. The latter then went his way and the young man called up the spirit. The spirit agreed to do anything for him, provided he would keep it busy always – failing which it would eat him up. The young man had all his desires fulfilled in a few hours – had a palace built and furnished, a car made, etc. – and he was at a loss to know how to keep the spirit busy any more, as otherwise his life was in danger. In keeping the spirit busy, he could not even enjoy the wonderful things it had provided for him. Here is an exact parallel for the situation in which the modern millionaire finds himself (he has all the good things in the world, but has neither the time nor the tranquillity to enjoy them, as the ghost of ambition keeps him working all the time). The young man thought of the yogi, who appeared and gave him some secret advice. As soon as the spirit appeared after the last mission, the young man asked it to erect a big pillar in front of the house, and to climb up and down till he asked it to stop. That was the yogi's solution; and that defeated the restless spirit.

We have such a restless spirit in us, and it is the impure desire-filled mind. If we do not keep it busy with some good activity continuously, it will create impure desires and thoughts and destroy us. The best way to keep it constantly busy, without obstructing our daily work, is japa of god's name or a mantra. This will not only keep evil thoughts, emotions and desires away, but it will enable us to enjoy righteous pleasures as only a peaceful mind can.

What is a mantra? This word has several meanings. It has been defined as 'anything that protects when the whole mind is saturated with it'. It may even mean 'a wholesome advice' (like the one the yogi gave the boy in the story). Popularly, it is a formula, a phrase or a word which has mystical if not magical properties: usually the name or a word-symbol of a deity is woven into it. Many of the mantras have an interesting and significant feature – as in the mantra oṁ namaḥ śivāya (salutation to Siva), there is no 'I'.

Here are a few popular mantras: oṁ, oṁ tat saṭ, sohaṁ, oṁ namaḥ śivāya, oṁ namo nārāyaṇāya, oṁ namo bhagavate vāsudevāya, oṁ śrī rāṁ jaya rāṁ jaya jaya rāṁ, hari oṁ, kyrie eleison christe eleison, oṁ jesus, jesus est avec moi, ya Allah, allah-u akbar, adonai elehaino adonai ekhad, oṁ mani padme hūṁ, la ilahi ill-allah-u. Select any you like, according to your taste, temperament and tradition.

As soon as you wake up in the morning start repeating the mantra, even in bed. Then, after having a quick wash, sit down and repeat the mantra for half an hour. During the day, every hour or so, close your eyes for just a few minutes and repeat the mantra.

The greatest secret in mantra-repetition is to associate the mantra with the breath. If yours is a short mantra repeat it once while you breathe in and once while you breathe out; if it is a long one, repeat half while you breathe in and half while you breathe out, but without 'breaking' into two. If you do this deliberately for a little while a conditioned reflex will be formed and the mind will enjoy the habit of mantra-repetition. You will soon create a habit this way and ultimately the mind will go on repeating the mantra along with your daily activities, as a sort of undercurrent. Even during sleep the mind will involuntarily go on repeating the mantra. This purifies and steadies the mind and enables you to enjoy great peace and happiness. Before going to bed repeat the mantra for about half an hour. You will have sound sleep and the 'current' will be kept up during the sleep too!

There are at least three ways in which japa is done. (1) The mantra is repeated audibly. (2) It is uttered silently but with a slight lip-movement. (3) It is repeated mentally. The masters declare that mental repetition is the most powerful, obviously because it leads to deep concentration of the mind.

All these mantras can also be sung aloud. Then it is known as kīrtan or saṅkīrtan, especially when several devotees sing in chorus. (Kīrtan also includes singing the praise of the lord, singing the psalms and hymns, and not necessarily mantras only). Many holy men are great votaries of this mode of devotion. Some of them sing and dance themselves into rapturous ecstasy.

My master Swami Sivananda lays the greatest emphasis on the repetition of the lord's names. This is also a great blessing to all who experience the stress and strain in the modern world. The strain is built up as we carry it over from one activity to another, from one piece of work to another. My master did not do that. As soon as one task came to an end he withdrew himself into this background of japa and rested in it for a few seconds before turning to another task. Thus the carry-over is cut off, we do not suffer the least strain, and we do not have a nervous breakdown. When the limbs are worked out after a period of activity they naturally ask for sleep and rest; and since the mind has been trained to withdraw into the background of màntra, the moment the last task of the day is done it immediately slips into the background, and we enjoy sound sleep.

23. FROM MANTRA TO MEDITATION

The mental japa protects the devotee from his own ego-sense and saves him from assuming that the ego-sense (which is a shadow) is substance or reality. How does it do that? By leading to meditation.

While you repeat the mantra mentally, enquire within yourself "What is the meaning of the expression – 'I am mentally repeating the mantra'?" You know what verbally uttering the mantra means; but what is 'mental' repetition, how is the sound of the mantra produced?

You will naturally realise that the mind or the intelligence in you utters the mantra, it reflects the mantra, it has identified itself with the mantra. You do not know what that intelligence is, and you realise that it is useless building an image of it and then pretending to know what it is. But, when you do mental japa the mantra and the mind become one, and by enquiring into the nature of the mantra (which is inwardly audible and therefore real) you are able to know what that inner intelligence really is. Be careful. For, if the mind produces a verbal answer, the enquiry is interrupted. Verbal answer is a description or a distraction; it is not the reality.

The inner intelligence produces the sound of the mantra, and the same intelligence is able to listen to it. When the attention is focussed upon that aspect of this intelligence which repeats the mantra, you think 'I am repeating the mantra'. When the same attention is shifted to that aspect of the intelligence which listens to the mantra, you think 'I am listening to the mantra'. Then you hear the noise of feet moving on the floor (or such external noise). Watch very carefully now. If you are watching intently, you can almost see something jumping up and down within you. (It is like when a movie camera is shaken – the figures suddenly become indistinct.) This is the psychological moment at which the concentration is threatened. If you are not careful at that moment you will wake up half an hour later and wonder "Oh, what happened to my mantra?"

If this is to be prevented, one must learn to recognise when the mantra becomes indistinct. The moment of distraction is the most important and vital phenomenon. If you are able to recognise it, your attention will not be distracted.

We return to mental japa. You are repeating the mantra. You hear it. Are you one or two? Now you are trying to examine the phenomenon of space that divides the mental repetition of the mantra from the mental hearing. You are looking at the division with great intensity and concentration. Suddenly the division disappears. The whole being repeats the mantra. You become one with the mantra. Your individual or separate personality is dissolved in the mantra.

Paramahamsa Muktananda describes the technique of doing japa in the four bodies, in his book, "Light on the Path":

"The four bodies of the soul are: the gross, the subtle, the causal, and the supracausal bodies. The physical body about five feet in size composed of five elementary constituents and red in colour, is the soul's gross body. The subtle body is about the size of a thumb, white in colour, and is located in the region of the throat. The causal body resides in the heart, is black in colour and about half the size of the joint of the thumb. The fourth one, situated in the navel region, is bluish in colour and about the size of a grain of lentil or a tiny spot.

When japa (repetition of a mantra) of the gross body, as recited by the tongue, enters further inside and begins to be repeated in the throat, it is known as japa of the subtle body. When this happens the sāḍhaka (practitioner) should understand that japa yoga has purified the gross body and has now entered the subtle body. Here the number of japa increases many times. During the japa in the throat the sāḍhaka experiences a divine tanḍrā. In this state he experiences a spell of blissful sleep and sometimes in that spell he gets visions of god, goddesses, the guru and other siddhas and saints. The japa of the throat goes on continuously day and night without a break.

After this, when the subtle body is thoroughly purified, japa goes still deeper and now it occurs in the heart. The place where japa continues is the sāḍhaka's third or causal body. This region is also known as the seat of deep sleep. The seeds of all the evils which cause one to go round and round in the cycle of birth and death are also there. The japa of the heart not only strengthens the body and adds lustre to the eyes and the face, but also makes the sāḍhaka do adventurous things. Usually one falls asleep during japa, yet the repetition of mantra maintains its continuity.

When the required number of japa of the third body is completed, it moves to the fourth or navel region. From the spiritual point of view this region of the navel is of great importance. The bluish lustrous body is also perceived within. Japa in this fourth body gives the sāḍhaka varied visions of divine lights. The light is also the light of Brahman, sometimes described as the supreme light of japa.

During sāḍhana (practice) in the fourth body the vibrations of japa are also felt in the head. By the power of japa in the navel region, all the hidden shaktis (powers) are awakened. At this stage, as a gift from the guru, the sāḍhaka gets a sort of mantra in the form of continuous awareness of his own self. This mantra is a prize medal from the benign and gracious guru. As an immediate consequence, the disciple is entirely transmuted."

Such transmutation is the real meaning of the word 'mantra'.

The ancient wisdom of the yogi has already given us these two powerful forces (prayer and repetition of the mantra) to help us deal with our own impure mind and enrich our daily life with peace and happiness.

There have been great masters in the world who have exalted bhakti yoga (and particularly japa) above all other spiritual practices. They believe that japa alone is sufficient for attaining the highest end and aim of yoga. Yet, anyone who has tried to do japa would know that a wandering mind is the worst enemy of japa, of bhakti, of yoga; and japa needs to be supported by other practices which fall under the category of haṭha yoga and rāja yoga.

☆☆☆☆☆☆☆☆☆☆

Chapter Four

HAṬHA YOGA

24. HAṬHA YOGA: AN ART AND A SCIENCE

Haṭha yoga has been widely advertised as a perfectly scientific way to health, relaxation and peace of mind, and by many people it is considered as a system of mainly physical exercise. Haṭha yoga certainly gives you a healthy body and a healthy mind, but its goal is different and much higher.

The physical postures and the breathing exercises of haṭha yoga calm the nerves and ease the tensions in our body and mind, and are vitally important, but we should not stop with them. We should go deeper and obtain the precious pearl we have within ourselves – self realisation.

These apparently simple postures and regulation of the breathing help in a wonderful way in our meditation and concentration. They who regularly follow up the yoga āsanas and prāṇāyāma with a period of concentration and meditation – and they alone – can understand this.

The Gheraṇḍa Saṁhitā lists the following seven as the aims of haṭha yoga: (1) purification through the six practices, (2) firmness through the practice of the yoga postures, (3) steadiness through the practice of mudrā, (4) courage and patience through the practice of introversion of the mind and the senses, (5) lightness through the regulation of the life force, (6) self-realisation through meditation and (7) freedom from bondage through the direct experience of cosmic consciousness, or samāḍhi.

In the scriptures there are declarations that the practitioner will conquer old age and death. This conquest is not to be confused with the physical immortality, nor is it a promise of perennial youth. It is the discovery of that which is untouched by old age and death.

Haṭha yoga enables you to discover health which is wholeness and holiness. It is a state of inner being in which there is no division at all, but only perfect balance and harmony. This wholeness or harmony concerns not only oneself but one's relation with the all, with the totality of existence.

Health (as also peace, bliss, love and god) is impossible to describe: the description is not 'health'. It has to be discovered and experienced. Even so, peace has to be discovered; love and bliss and god have to be discovered. Haṭha yoga is a method and a technique for this discovery.

Haṭha yoga manifests on two levels at the same time — – the physical body and the subtle body. The physical body is material, the subtle body is the combination of the energy and intelligence that indwell the physical body and animate it. The 'discovery' on the level of the physical body happens when the toxins that cover the cells of the body are eliminated. The 'discovery' on the subtle level reveals the mysterious and mighty intelligence that uses the life force to animate the body and to perform the numerous functions on the physical level.

Even the simplest movement of the body, like lifting one foot up while standing, is not the work of the muscles alone. When this simple movement is performed with great inward attention, you immediately see the wondrous function of the intelligence that is inherent in every cell of your body, which springs into action to restore the balance. You cannot imitate this action with both your feet on the ground. Hence, it is clear that that intelligence is beyond the 'me' (the ego-sense) and that it responds only to real need, not to imaginery situations. The discovery of this intelligence and the direct realisation of its incredible power and efficiency is the conquest of old age and death, worry and anxiety. That intelligence knows what to do and how to do it.

Even the physical aspect of haṭha yoga is so designed as to work on the internal vital organs rather than the superficial muscles. The health of the body depends to a great extent on the health of the nervous system and of the endocrine system of ductless glands. This is done by ensuring that the life force or prāṇa flows through these organs without being blocked or rushed. If the prāṇic pressure is even and harmonious, then the body and the mind function well.

Prāṇa is life. It is the power in the life-breath. It bears the same relation to the nerves and the body as the electrical current bears to the electric wire. You do not see the current; you cannot see the prāṇa either – but you see the function of electricity in the lights, fans, radio, television; you see the function of the prāṇa in the countless faculties and functions you enjoy in your life.

Prāṇa flows through nāḍīs which are like light-waves or sound-waves. If the prāṇa flows freely you are full of life, cheerful, happy, peaceful, optimistic and zealous; you look forward to facing the challenge of life with hope and enthusiasm.

The yoga system of physical culture waters the roots of inner health, so that the yogi's powers of resistance and endurance are much higher than those of others. He enjoys an inner sense of well-being. This system enables you to prevent illness in youth and in old age to rise above such illness.

As well as concentrating on the glands, haṭha yoga also strengthen the nerves by working on the brain and spinal column from which the nerves branch off. Glands, brain and spinal column are therefore our primary concern, though we do pay some attention to several important internal viscera, expecially those connected with digestion.

However, a serious student would insist that he has nothing whatsoever to do with glands, nerves and the digestive system and that he is not interested in strengthening them. His attention is focussed on the nāḍīs and the cakras (which the layman associates with the nerves and glands) and the solar plexus or gastric fire. His aim is to purify these nāḍīs. In their pure state they are strong, powerful, efficient and radiant.

25. *PURIFICATORY EXERCISES*

Prāṇa is very much like a magnetic field in and around us. This prāṇa 'flows' and those streams themselves are nāḍīs. The student of yoga should observe this magnetic field with keen attention and become sensitive to any disruptions that may occur in that field due to faulty environment, wrong food or unhealthy and unholy mental or physical activity.

Such a disruption needs appropriate healing exercise or remedial measure. The hatha yoga scriptures give several purificatory exercises. Six of these exercises have been described in both the Haṭha Yoga Pradīpikā and in the Gheraṇḍa Saṁhitā. They are: (1) dhauti, (2) vasti, (3) neti, (4) nauli or lauliki, (5) trāṭaka and (6) kapālabhāti. Gheraṇḍa Saṁhitā gives not only several variations but elaborations and subdivisions in these. For instance, dhauti (washing) is subdivided into internal cleaning, cleaning the teeth, cleaning the heart and cleaning the rectum. It also describes several variations of the dhauti using different elements: air, water, cloth and a twig. As some of these need expert guidance, the technique given below is brief.

Dhauti

TECHNIQUE: 1. Drink air as you drink water. Retain it in the stomach for a short while. Then expel it through the rectum.

2. Drink water, till it fills 'up to the throat'. Shake the abdomen. Expel the water through the rectum.

3. Vigorously draw the navel back towards the spine and relax. Do this in quick succession one hundred times. It is like fanning the gastric fire.

The above three are methods for internal cleaning, using air, water and 'fire' respectively.

4. Cleaning the teeth. This includes cleaning of the teeth with catechu powder or pure earth, scraping the tongue right

up to the throat with the fingers, cleaning of the ears with the index and ring fingers, and cleaning the frontal sinuses by rubbing the forehead near the bridge of the nose. (The text also prescribes the gentle pulling of the tongue to lengthen it gradually.)

5. Cleaning of the heart is really cleaning of the throat and the stomach. This is done in three different ways. (i) A thin stalk of plantain or tumeric is inserted down the gullet and drawn out slowly. (ii) After a meal, drink water 'up to the neck' and vomit it. (iii) Take a long strip of thin cloth about three inches wide and fifteen cubits long. Wet it. Swallow it slowly. Draw it out again.

6. Cleaning of the rectum. Using a piece of tumeric root or the middle finger, clean the rectum with water.

BENEFITS: These cleansing exercises promote the health and efficiency of the organs thus cleaned. Disorders caused by phlegm and bile are remedied. Digestion, assimilation and elimination improve. The movement of prāṇa is made efficient.

Vasti

TECHNIQUE: Vasti is the cleaning of the large intestines. It is of two kinds: (i) Seated in water up to the navel assume the utkaṭāsana (resting the body on the toes and the buttocks on the heels). Contract and dilate the rectum, to draw the water into the colon. After a little while expel the water. (ii) Practise the paścimottāna āsana. Move the intestines from side to side and at the same time do the aśvinī mudrā – contract and dilate the rectum.

BENEFITS: The cleansing effect is obvious. The text says that it promotes clarity of the senses and the mind.

Neti

TECHNIQUE: Take a piece of thread. Close one nostril and gently insert the thread through the other nostril. When the end of the thread reaches the throat, catch hold of it and pull it through the mouth.

BENEFITS: Neti clears the nasal passages and sinuses. The text claims that it helps develop extra-sensory-perception.

Nauli

TECHNIQUE: Practise uḍḍīyāna bandha. Isolate the rectus abdomini and let it drop forward. You may then 'churn' this. The technique is described in greater detail elsewhere in this section.

BENEFITS: The text calls this 'the crown of haṭha yoga practice' and credits it with the ability to destroy all diseases and restore harmony.

Trāṭaka

TECHNIQUE: Look with unwinking eyes at a small object till tears flow from the eyes.

BENEFITS: It improves eyesight and powers of concentration.

Kapālabhāti

TECHNIQUE: Three types are described in Gheraṇḍa Saṁhitā: (i) Inhale through the left nostril, exhale through the right; inhale through the right and exhale through the left, in quick succession. (ii) Draw water through both nostrils and expel it through the mouth slowly. (iii) Sip water through the mouth and expel it through the nostrils. The Haṭha Yoga Pradīpikā, however, prescribes rapid inhalation and exhalation like the bellows of a blacksmith, which makes it look very much like the bhastrikā prāṇāyāma. However, if the student remembers that kapālabhāti means 'that which makes the skull shine' it will be clear that in kapālabhāti the attention is focussed on the head: the rapid breathing must clear the head.

BENEFITS: Phlegmatic condition is remedied. The text says that the practitioner never grows old but will have a radiant body.

The Haṭha Yoga Pradīpikā says that when the nāḍīs are purified the body becomes slim and radiant, retention of the breath (during the practice of prāṇāyāma) is made easy, the mystic fire is kindled and the practitioner hears the subtle mystic sounds.

26. SIVANANDA'S WAY

The next aspect of haṭha yoga is yoga āsana.

The motivation for the practice of the yoga postures varies from one practitioner to the other. Depending upon the motivation the student's approach to haṭha yoga is also bound to vary. There are some who devote several hours a day to the practice of the yoga postures. Others devote a few minutes. There are some yoga teachers and students who insist that the body must be forced to obey the practitioner's will, while others feel that the yoga āsanas should be practised without the least strain.

Swami Sivananda sought the subtle middle path, which reconciled these views. The wise student of yoga neither forces the body, nor leaves it alone: he educates it and gently uncovers (discovers) the hidden potentialities of the indwelling intelligence. There is no pain in the process and therefore there is no resistance. The will-force is not used. There is an inner awareness which detects the obstacles and removes them.

This is also the attitude and the approach of the great yogi Desikachar of Madras (the son and disciple of the well known yogi Krishnamacharya).

It is possible that the stirring to action of a disused part of the body is experienced as discomfort. It is also possible that when toxins are eliminated by the action of the yoga postures this is experienced as discomfort. The student's sensitivity should read the message correctly and not treat this as pain or the sign of the body's inability.

When you observe the effect of the yoga postures on the body you see that in each posture the inner intelligence springs into action and that often manifests as the dual action of extension and tension. The student realises that this action of intelligence is neither relaxation nor tension but both, appropriately.

If one practises the yoga postures in order to increase the self-awareness, then the practice should be characterised by great gentleness, worshipfulness, thankfulness to the divine, discovery of one's potentialities and the education of the body so that it reaches out to its maximum capacity – without pain or strain, but with curiosity and an eagerness to treat each posture as a fresh challenge. This is done by performing every exercise of body and breath 'mindfully'. When done this way, they enable you to cultivate a special, non-possessive awareness of the body and to learn the art of looking within.

The following pages give a description of a few basic yoga āsanas. It is possible to derive great benefit if you devote from half to one hour to the entire series, though you can spend longer if you wish. Or you can select one posture for special attention on each day of the week, while not neglecting the other postures.

A suggested sequence for practice is āsana, prāṇāyāma, mudrā and then meditation. It is unwise to do the āsanas after prāṇāyāma or meditation. The best period for practice is either in the early morning or in the evening, however it is important that the āsanas are not practised within two hours after a meal.

There are no 'dangers' in the practice of these postures. If you are attentive to the message of your body and sensitive to the action of the postures on the body, you will know what to do and what not to do. The intelligence in the body will not allow you to injure your body.

27. I WORSHIP THE SUN, THE GIVER OF LIFE SŪRYANAMASKĀRA

In the system of 'sūryanamaskāra' are combined several yoga postures with rhythmic breathing, rapid movement, sunbathing and prayerful contemplation of the divine power that the sun represents. We are asked to practise this sūryanamaskāra facing the morning sun, bathing our whole body in the life-giving rays of the sun, the giver of light, life, joy and warmth to the whole world.

Sūryanamaskāra consists of twelve postures or stages. One posture smoothly and gracefully flows into the next. There is fairly vigorous movement which builds up the muscles too, yet it conforms to the vitally important rule in yoga that there should be no undue strain or violence in the practice. Hence, the extraordinary and unique result: after the practice, one does not feel tired and exhausted as it often happens in mere physical culture, but one feels thoroughly refreshed.

Of still greater importance is the inner mood with which sūryanamaskāra is done. Inwardly watch every little movement, becoming aware of every change that takes place in the body, especially the spine. The mind must be quiet and observant to do this, and after a few months practice, this awareness will grow.

TECHNIQUE: (1) Stand upright. Fold the palms in front of the chest, as in the oriental way of greeting. Exhale. (2) Inhaling all the way, swing your arms up above your head, bending the trunk from the base gradually up the vertebrae as far back as you can. (Exhaling, if begun towards the end of this movement, will enable you to bend a little more.) (3) Extend upwards and then forward, stretching the spine and breathing out. Without bending your knees, place the palms of your hands squarely on the ground, fingers pointing straight in front, parallel to the feet. Bury the face between the knees. (4) Throw right leg back, while inhaling. Flex the left leg at the knee and let the thigh be in close contact with the torso. Look up. Inhale. (5) Throw the left leg also back. Straighten the back and the arms. Breathe out. (6) As you breathe out, flex at the elbows. Dip the whole body and touch the ground with your forehead, chest, palms, knees and toes. The other parts of the body should not touch the ground. Keep the 'tail' up, giving a pelvic tilt. (7) Swing the head up and backwards, straighten the arms and bending the spine backwards as much as possible: inhale. (8) As you breathe out, swing the hip up and back and assume the inverted V position, the feet and palms resting on the floor. (9) Bring the right leg forward, foot flat on floor between the hands (as 4 above). Inhale. (10) Bring left leg forward, straighten knees, head down (as 3 above). Exhale. (11) Inhale, straighten the body, and swing your arms up above your head, bending back as far as possible (as 2 above). (12) Stand upright (as 1 above). Now resume the normal standing position. Repeat this at least twelve times every morning, alternating legs.

28. THE YOGI'S FAVOURITE
ŚIRASĀSANA

The first and perhaps foremost of the yoga āsanas is śirasāsana, for it has an immediate effect on the brain, man's most distinguishing feature.

The head is also the control tower for the rest of the body and is the root of the nervous system. It also contains two endocrine glands of the greatest importance to the whole body, the pituitary gland and the pineal gland.

By practising śirasāsana the yogi strives to keep the brain and these glands strong, so that he can utilise them to their fullest capacity.

TECHNIQUE: It is good to do the head-stand by stages, though young people might regard this as a waste of time and might be able to do the perfect headstand on the first attempt.

STAGE ONE: Spread a folded blanket on the floor. Lock the fingers of your two hands while squatting on your knees. Lean forward and place this finger–lock with the little fingers on the floor, and the finger-lock itself at right angles to the floor. Rest the forearms on the floor, making an equilateral triangle. Now, let your head rest on the blanket, not on your palms (please remember that the palms and finger–lock are meant only to help you maintain your balance). The two palms together 'cup' the back of your head. Lift your knees off the floor. 'Walk' in till the knees touch your chest. Do this for a few days or weeks. Do not try to lift the toes off the floor. Try to make the back and the spinal column as perpendicular to the floor as possible.

STAGE TWO: As soon as you are able to walk freely without the legs becoming stiff and tense, you can proceed to the next stage. Bring the knees to your chest. Tense your torso, not the legs. Gently lift the toes off the floor. Do not be in a hurry. Do not kick. It might help you if you hold your breath as you are attempting to lift the toes off the floor (but remember that great masters of yoga like Shri Iyengar rightly disapprove of holding the breath during postures). Every attempt you make improves the muscles of your torso. If you are able to lift your feet off the floor, repeat the entire movement a few times.

STAGE THREE: When you are able to do this quite easily, then proceed to the next stage. With the calf muscles still in contact with the thighs, lift up the legs till the thighs are parallel to the ground. Gradually, with the legs still folded at the knees, straighten them till from head to knee is perpendicular. Then straighten the legs.

Every time you practise the head-stand, please make sure that the floor is even, that there is a firm, soft padding under your head and that there are no hairpins etc., on your head.

When you have reached stage three, hold the posture for a few seconds to begin with and increase this period by about a minute a week, till you can comfortably hold it for about five minutes. Come down slowly. Rest.

CAUTION: Do not attempt the full head-stand (stage three) if you suffer from blood pressure or from a heavy 'head' cold. Be content with stages one and two till the condition improves.

CONCENTRATION: While standing on the head, concentrate on the brain itself, particularly the pineal and the pituitary glands.

BENEFITS: It is impossible to describe all the benefits that one can derive from this posture. The mental action involved in the concentration sends an abundant supply of prāṇic energy to the head, thus vitalising the brain (which is the seat of the thinking faculty) and the two glands which have a lot to do with our emotional balance. The head takes advantage of the gravity of the earth and draws to itself an abundant supply of blood from the heart; all the parts are nourished and strengthened, and there is an increased flow of energy and its circulation in the brain. The abdominal viscera,which have become sluggish on account of the intra-abdominal pressure of the thoracic organs,regain their tone. The eyes, neck, ears, nose ,etc. are also strengthened. Muscles of the neck, back and shoulders—which play no part at all while we stand, walk, sit or sleep—get their exercise in this unusual posture. Brain power, memory and intellectual faculties lying dormant in the head are awakened and enhanced.

Regular practise of this posture imparts lustre and smoothness to the face and removes wrinkles. Though this is true of the whole system of yoga, this particular posture greatly strengthens the will power. In the yoga system, the parts of the body which are usually regarded as beyond one's power to influence are brought under control. This strengthens our will power, self-confidence and optimism.

29. THE YOGI'S TONIC
SARVĀṄGĀSANA

Sarvāṅgāsana works primarily on the glands of our throat – the thyroid and para-thyroid glands, which are situated at the base of the neck astride the windpipe. The thyroid gland works in close harmony with the pituitary gland, and together they are largely responsible for our physical and emotional well-being. The para-thyroids control the calcium content in the body.

Our neck is the slender link between the head and heart. It is from the neck that the brain flows down the backbone as the spinal cord. It is in the neck that we have the vocal cords, and the neck hides within it pipe-lines for the flow of breath and blood. Hence the importance of a pose that concentrates on this region.

TECHNIQUE: STAGE ONE: Lie down flat on your back. Inhaling, tense your abdominal muscles and lift the feet off the floor. Hold them at the 45 degrees position for a few seconds; relax. Repeat a few times.

STAGE TWO: If that is easy enough, now proceed. Inhaling, tense your abdominal muscles and lift the feet off the floor till they are perpendicular, at right angles to the floor. Your 'tail' must still be on the floor. Hold it for a few seconds, then drop the feet to the floor. Do this a few times.

STAGE THREE: If that is easy enough, now proceed with the next step. Using the hands as little as possible i.e., without digging them into the floor and without pushing the body up with them, but with help of the abdominal muscles alone, lift the legs off the floor; lift the waist also up. Gently, but firmly hold your waist with your hands. If your elbows are spread out too far to the sides, they have no power to support the body. Bring them close to each other. Once you are used to this posture you can breathe normally and maintain the posture for a long time (over half an hour). Begin with a few seconds and increase the time gradually. Returning to the original position lower your legs a little over your head, but not right down to the floor. Drop the arms flat on the ground. Gently exhale. 'Unwind' the whole body, using your abdominal muscles again. Do not let the body drop on the floor, and try not to lift your head off the floor. This is half shoulder stand which is an excellent posture, especially for womenfolk who suffer from abdominal troubles and for those who suffer from varicose veins.

STAGE FOUR: If that becomes easy, then try this one. Again, using the hands as little as possible, lift up your legs and waist off the floor, and swing them over and back till they are well away from the floor. Fold the arms at the elbows and balance your body with your hands. Straighten your legs now. Gently but firmly push the torso towards the chin, all the time straightening the whole body. You must breathe normally. Relax the neck and shoulders and ensure that they lie flat on the carpet.

CONCENTRATE on the neck, the thyroid gland and the parathyroids.

Return to the original position as in Stage 3. Relax. As you relax, feel that the energy that was concentrated at the throat during the posture is being distributed throughout the body. Remain relaxed for a few seconds or a minute or two.

Remember that we are dealing with yoga postures, not movements, not exercises. A posture is for being held: a posture repeated becomes more of a movement. This is unavoidable in the beginning; but the central principle should not be forgotten. When the posture is held, the yogi feels that certain parts of the body are squeezed, tensed and relaxed. The posture is obviously not the way the body is normally; hence sectors of the body which did not receive attention in one's normal life, do so now. This attention (which is different from tension) draws the mysterious lifeforce or prāṇa to these sectors of the body. Such attention is effective only if the posture is held for a few minutes at least; if there is constant movement, the attention is disturbed and the benefit is lost.

Sarvāṅgāsana can be held for a considerable time, but in the beginning it is better to repeat it a few times instead. If it is held for over two minutes, then follow it up with matsyāsana or fish posture.

BENEFITS: Sarvāṅgāsana has nearly all the benefits of śirasāsana, plus the wonderful effect on the glands of the throat. It also relieves asthma, colds, bronchitis and nasal troubles.

The intensification of circulation in the area of the glands promotes their more efficient functioning. The yogi achieves this by concentrating his attention on the glands concerned, which is the best way to ensure that the prāṇa flows to the glands. This should be remembered in the case of all the other yoga āsanas, too.

30. HEALTHY PLANTS GROW FROM HEALTHY ROOTS
HALĀSANA

The yogi's whole attention is concentrated on the nerves. The spinal nerves are the roots of the branches that act on the various parts of the body, and the health of the latter depends entirely on the health of the former.

It is comparatively easy to keep the spine healthy, but once the mobility of the vertebral bones is lost, the various parts of the body become less active. That is perhaps why we feel so refreshed and vigorous after practising halāsana, it restores the mobility.

TECHNIQUE: Start as for sarvāṅgāsana (the shoulder stand). As you lift the legs up, instead of merely pointing them up, lower them above your head, till the toes touch the floor behind the head. Keep the knees straight and close together. Press the chest against the chin. The arms rest where they were when you were lying down.

BREATHING: Inhale. Exhale slowly as you commence the posture. When you complete the exhalation, your toes touch the floor. In the beginning, you may have to raise the toes off the floor while breathing in. With a little (but regular) practice, it should be possible to breathe normally while holding this posture.

BENEFITS: The thyroid gland is massaged by the prāṇa that is directed to it when you concentrate your mind on it. The back muscles and the spinal nerves are exercised and strengthened. It has a beneficial influence on the sympathetic nervous system too. In addition, it tones up the digestive apparatus. The pressure of the thorax on the abdomen is relaxed. The abdomen itself is lightly (because it is lifted up) and firmly massaged: the 'idle' blood accumulated in that region is thrown back into circulation. The tone of all the digestive organs is improved: this posture can cure all the maladies that originate or thrive on digestive disturbances.

A person's metabolic rate is largely dependent on the functions of the glands, in particular the thyroid. That is why the shoulder stand and the plough are so important, for these two give a gentle squeeze to the thyroid gland and invigorate it. This posture also tones up the adrenal glands.

Till you become proficient in this posture, you can practise it a few times (like an exercise), retaining it for a few seconds each time. Once you are proficient in it and you are able to breathe normally during the posture, it is good to hold the posture for a few minutes. But, then, immediately after this you must do the fish posture.

An advanced stage of this posture is: first do the halāsana or plough posture. Relax. Drop the knees down till they touch the ears. Lift the hands off the ground, bring them above the head, and lock the fingers, keeping the hands close to the calf muscles.

CONCENTRATION: The backbone, mainly. You can actually visualise the muscles of the back relax, allowing the spinal nerves more freedom and activity. You can also concentrate on the thyroid, the adrenals and the abdomen.

CAUTION: Be gentle. If you are violent, you might lose your balance and roll on your sides, and perhaps sprain your neck. The more relaxed you are the better and easier it is to do this posture.

As you relax you will notice your shoulders and the back of your neck dropping flat on the carpet, and the uncomfortable pressure in the neck suddenly ceasing.

Do not be impatient to achieve perfection in a day!

Return to the normal position as in the case of sarvāṅgāsana.

31. A DIVINE MARVEL
MATSYĀSANA

Matsyāsana or the fish posture is complementary to sarvāṅgāsana and halāsana, but it also has its own unique advantages. Man does not use his lungs correctly; and wrong sitting, standing and walking have all conspired to produce shallow breathing.

In the matsyāsana or fish posture, the yogi corrects this inefficient breathing. The pose achieves a double purpose; not only does it stretch the chest and throat, but it also gives a gentle squeeze to the back, and the all-important suprarenal glands.

TECHNIQUE: This is generally done in the lotus posture or padmāsana (which is: sit on the ground, flex the legs at the knees, bringing the right foot on to the left thigh and the left foot on to the right thigh), when it is very effective. But, if the lotus posture is not possible, sit with the legs stretched in front. Bend backward till the crown of your head touches the ground and the chest arches away from the floor. Rest the elbows on the ground and press them firmly thus raising and throwing the chest out fully. If the lotus posture is possible, hold the toes while resting the elbows on the ground. If a slight feeling of dizziness is experienced by the beginner, try easing gently up into the fish posture from a lying down position and hold only for a few seconds at first until the balance mechanism of the ears is adjusted. If you cannot manage this, try the half fish posture – sitting back on your heels resting on palms placed on the floor behind you, arch the spine and head back while remaining seated.

CONCENTRATION is on the lungs, thyroid and also on the back, specially the suprarenal glands.

BREATHING: Normal. Do not allow the rib cage to collapse when you exhale. Breathe with the lungs themselves, using a minimum movement of the diaphragm (i.e. the abdomen).

BENEFITS: The neck which was 'crushed' forward by the shoulder stand and the plough posture, gets a reversed movement; and is stretched now. The massage of the thyroid, parathyroids, the vocal chords, the adenoids and the tonsils, is completed by these alternate crushing and stretching movements. This massage invites greater blood circulation to those parts, thus stimulating their proper activity.

Regular practice of the matsyāsana prevents the numerous ills that afflict our respiratory system, including asthma, pneumonia, pleurisy and tuberculosis.

The yoga practitioner does matsyāsana and holds it for half the duration of the previous two (viz. the shoulder stand and the plough pose).

CAUTION: Those who have goitre should be careful.

32. *UNLOCK THE HIDDEN TREASURE*
BHUJANGĀSANA

The fountain of wisdom is in us. Great power is hidden in us. Health is within us, not in the bottle at the drug store. How few of us do really unlock this hidden treasure.

Two factors promote the proper funcioning of the spinal nerves: (a) the mobility of vertebrae and (b) the health of the muscles in the back. If the vertebrae lose their mobility, they impinge on one another. If the muscles lose their tone and become rigid, they impede the functioning of not only the vital spinal nerves, but also several of the vital blood vessels and the inner viscera. The trunk contains the sympathetic and the para-sympathetic nervous system. These are in charge of all the vital functions of the body and work in complete harmony. One raises the blood pressure; the other lowers it. One gives the chest the command to expand, so that you can breathe in; the other gives the counter-command, so that you can breathe out. Both these opposite actions are necessary in order to preserve harmony!

The autonomous nervous system lies close to the spinal column. There are two plexuses of nerves, one in the cervical region and the other in the lumbar region, besides several other plexuses along the spine, which are of special importance. The yogis regard these plexuses as the physical counterparts of 'psychic energy diffusion centres'.

You cannot think of the trunk, without considering kidneys and the suprarenal glands themselves. Cortisone is manufactured by these glands. In health, they have their own medical board of which the pituitary, the thyroid and the adrenal glands are members; they consult one another and plan their life-saving activities. They are also closely related to the body's vital communication system, the sympathetic nerves. Anger, shock, fear, passion, all act upon the adrenals.

The suprarenal glands, in fact, seem to control all the functions of body, either directly or indirectly through the other glands like the pituitary, the thyroid and the gonads. How essential it is, then, to keep them healthy! But how? Here is the yogi's answer: bhujangāsana (the cobra posture).

TECHNIQUE: Lie face downwards on a carpet, forehead touching the carpet. Place the palms of the hands by the side of the shoulders. Relax. Roll the head backward (caution: do not lift it). You will feel intense pressure on the middle parts of the spine and back. This pressure will slowly ascend as the upper part of the back bends over. Keep looking straight up and in front. Hold the posture for a few seconds. Roll forward, stomach first, chest, shoulders and then face. There should be no lifting, no dropping – but rolling all the time. Repeat this a few times. In the beginning (even if you are able to do it properly) you might feel a bit of a strain; but as you go on, you will notice it fills you with energy.

BREATHING: Should be normal though very light throughout.

CONCENTRATE: On the nerve-plexuses in the cervical region, the solar plexus just behind the stomach, the adrenal glands and the lumbar region.

In addition to strengthening the spinal nerves and the suprarenal glands, this will correct many defects of the spine.

33. MAINTENANCE OF THE NUTRITION FACTORY ŚALABHĀSANA AND DHANURĀSANA

In the bhujangāsana or cobra pose, we notice that the spine is curved backwards and pressure is exerted on the back muscles. The yogi is not complacent. He wants to make doubly sure that the vital glands and nerves within the back are benefited. Hence he follows the cobra pose with the locust posture (śalabhāsana).

TECHNIQUE: STAGE ONE: Lie down on your stomach. Let your chin rest on the floor. Clench your fists and place them under your thighs, with the elbows straight. Inhale, and simultaneously raise your left leg up, straight and stiff. Exhale and bring the leg down. Inhale while raising the right leg up. Exhale and relax. Repeat this a few times.

STAGE TWO: Lie down as before. Inhale. Press your hands down and with a powerful contraction of your abdominal muscles, gently but firmly, without jerks and without kicking, raise (not just lift) both your legs up as far as you can. Breathe gently. The Gheraṇḍa Saṁhitā mentions that you need raise your feet only half a yard from the floor. It will help if you feel that the weight of your body rests on your chin – try it.

A variation is to place the arms by the sides of the body and lift both legs and the shoulders up. Another variation is to raise the arms up too.

CONCENTRATE alternately on the solar plexus and the abdominal viscera.

BENEFITS: You can readily see that this is a powerful stimulant, not only to the solar plexus, but to the abdominal muscles and the vital digestive organs. The solar plexus is the biggest nerve centre in the body, aside from the brain, and is the ruler of the 'sympathetic system', the digestive organs and other vegetative functions. All these vital organs are interconnected: the adrenals, the sympathetic nervous system, the solar plexus, the digestive organs, the pituitary, the thyroid and the gonads. The yoga system exerts its beneficial influence upon all of them.

Try this pose and you might immediately realise that your abdominal walls have lost their tone, the muscles their strength, and the joints their flexibility. All these are vital to our health, happiness and long life. Try and try again: you will regain them. You will immediately feel a certain 'lightness' in the abdominal region, whatever its size. This is due to the fact that the nerves which had become sluggish on account of neglect have 'awakened'.

This posture (with the cobra posture and the bow posture which follows) can cure a host of digestive disorders, not by artificially stimulating the digestive organs themselves, but by filling the solar plexus with life. But please remember that the yogi wants to improve his digestion in order that he may eat less.

Dhanurāsana

The bow posture (dhanurāsana) supplements both the cobra and locust postures and makes sure that the solar plexus, the suprarenal glands and the abdominal (digestive) organs have all received their due share of prāṇa.

TECHNIQUE: STAGE ONE: Lie down on your stomach as before. Inhale. Raise your head and shoulders. Fold your left leg at the knee. Catch hold of your left ankle with your left hand. Hold your breath. Make a slow 'kicking' movement with your leg, stretching it out; avoid pulling the leg towards you; do not bend your arm. Feel the tensing of your left back muscles. Relax. Exhale. Do the same with the other arm and leg. Repeat the movements a few times. This is of special value to those who, on account of stiffness of their back, are unable to reach both their ankles together; they will usually find it easier to hold the ankles one by one. If they practise this for some weeks, they will be able to proceed to the next stage without difficulty.

STAGE TWO: Lie down on your stomach. Inhale. Raise your head and shoulders. Fold both your legs at the knees. Catch hold of the ankles with your hands. Hold the breath if necessary in the beginning. Gently and firmly stretch the legs without loosening the grip on your ankles. Your body will 'curl' up. Keep going till the entire torso is up above the ground. At the same time, by shifting your attention to the thighs, lift them up too. If you find this difficult, 'rock' forward. For this, keep your body tension high. If you relax, your thighs and your body will come down. If you keep the tension and 'rock', or 'roll' forward, your thighs will rise from the floor. Once you are able to lift the thighs up, you need not rock or roll. Hold the posture for a few seconds. Exhale and relax. Repeat this a few times.

BREATHING: When you are efficient you will not hold the breath at all. Breathe gently through the nose.

CONCENTRATE alternately on the solar plexus and abdominal viscera.

BENEFITS: One should practise this in order to realise what it can do. It gives a gentle but powerful squeeze to the entire back. It preserves the mobility of the vertebrae. The spinal nerve-roots are freed from intervertebral pressure. The autonomous nervous system becomes fully autonomous. The kidneys and the suprarenal glands are purified, vitalised and strengthened. (Indirectly the heart and the other ductless glands are also benefited). The solar plexus is given a gentle massage and the abdominal viscera are charged with power when you concentrate on them. The otherwise neglected lower parts of the spine, and particularly the sciatic nerve are exercised. A host of pelvic disorders (expecially in women) are prevented. That the muscles of the abdomen and the thighs are also benefited is a minor matter.

By working on the solar plexus and the abdominal organs these three postures, plus the next one (paścimottānāsana or forward bending posture) increase the anti-anaemic factor in the system.

34. HEALTH IS WITHIN REACH: BEND FORWARD PAŚCIMOTTĀNĀSANA

In this modern world where everything is made to order, sluggishness (which is euphemistically called comfort) and luxury, are the fashion. The vital organs in the abdomen yawn, turn over and go to sleep! Their demands are less and appetite fails. But modern man eats more, for he is the victim of his own habit and others' hospitality – and lands in a hospital! Paścimottānāsana will help to prevent this.

TECHNIQUE: Lie flat on your back, hands stretched above the head, parallel to each other. Inhale. Tighten the abdominal walls and muscles and raise the torso from the ground. Do not lift the legs off the ground, if possible. Keep the upper arms close to the ears. Keep the back straight. Stretch yourself up, tall and taller still, right from the tail. Bend the whole body forward, still stretching the back from the tail, keeping the head up, face looking at feet. Exhale. Bring the whole body down on the outstretched legs. With complete exhalation hold the ankles at least, with the knees straight and stiff. Do not strain yourself over much. What you can do today – the maximum – is best for you today. Gently hold the ankles, the calf muscles or the knees, and rhythmically and 'cyclically' relax and stretch the sides of the body, fixing the attention on the small of the back. Bend forward quickly again and bury the face between the knees. This does not depend upon the size of the belly at all, but on the suppleness of the hip-joint. If you can do this holding the ankles comfortably and bend forward, bend a little more and hold the heels and repeat the bending forward movement; lastly, hold the big toe (or all the toes) and bend forward. Once you have achieved this you will find that the āsana becomes easy of accomplishment and you can even hold it for a few seconds or minutes – when you can breathe softly throughout.

CONCENTRATION: Focus your attention on the small of the back during the first part and on the abdominal viscera during the posture.

BENEFITS: Yogis claim extraordinary spiritual and psychic benefits for this āsana. It has an extraordinary effect upon the sympathetic and parasympathetic nervous system and also the spinal cord – which the yogi regards as the most important 'nāḍī (psychic channel of power) in the body.

The liver and the spleen, the pancreas and the intestines receive a gentle squeeze. Whatever the size of the belly, it will not be sluggish. If it is pathological or psychological (result of compulsive eating) it will be reduced, without any drugging or dieting; if it is yours by inheritance, you will be unaware of its bulk.

We should not omit to mention the salutory effect this āsana has on the lowest end of the spinal column, on the sciatic nerve as also on the knee joint. All of them are wonderfully benefited by this āsana. The Haṭha Yoga Pradīpikā says that it makes the prāṇa flow through the suṣumnā or the central channel in the spine.

CAUTION: Anyone can practise this. One should be gentle, but bold and optimistic.

This is the counter-posture to the three previous ones. All of them together keep the hip joints flexible and vital,and senility at a distance.

35. THIS TWIST IS YOGA ARDHAMATSYENDRĀSANA

So far we have only dealt with forward and backward bending postures. The spinal column has another form of mobility, the twist. The twist not only completes the work on the spinal column, but also exerts the greatest influence on the sympathetic nerves and the parasympathetic vagus nerve as well.

TECHNIQUE: STAGE ONE: Sit with both legs stretched straight out in front of you. Bend the right leg drawing the right foot up level with the left knee. Turn left, keeping the spine straight, until the right shoulder is to the left of the right knee. Bring the right hand round behind the right side of the body until you can grasp it with the left hand. Look over the left shoulder. Repeat with the left leg bent and left arm circling around.

STAGE TWO: Sit on the floor with the legs stretched in front of you. Bend the right leg and place the right foot to the left of the left knee. Make sure that the foot is planted well on the floor. Bring the right hand behind the back and turn to the right. Bend the left arm and take it to the right of the right knee. With the elbow push the right knee to the left thus giving yourself added leverage to turn as far to the right as possible. Exhale as you begin to turn; breathe lightly when you hold the posture; inhale when you relax and resume the normal sitting position. Rest for a few seconds, then repeat to the other side.

STAGE THREE: Sit on the floor with legs outstretched. Fold the left leg at the knee and place the left foot at the root of the right thigh. Bend the right leg and place the right foot close to the left of the left knee. Take your right hand behind your back towards your left hip. Exhale, and turn to your right. Bring your left armpit on to your right knee and catch hold of the right ankle with your hand – the whole arm lies close to the right leg. Using this as a lever, turn as far to your right as you can. Exhale as you begin to turn; breathe gently as you hold the posture (for a few seconds); inhale as you relax. Rest for a few seconds and do it 'on the other side', turning to the left this time.

STAGE FOUR: Sit with the legs outstretched. Bend the left leg at the knee and place the left foot at the root of the right thigh (so that your right buttock rests on the left ankle). Draw up the right knee, place the right foot to the left of the left thigh as near to the left hip as possible. Bring the right arm behind the back and grasp the right ankle. Bring left armpit over the right knee and hold the left knee with the left hand. (Illustrated) Repeat on other side.

CAUTION: Avoid stooping. Keep the back straight. People with large abdomen and chest should tilt their body backward slightly as they begin to turn and then bring it forward; else the thigh will obstruct the chest.

BREATHING: Exhale as you begin to turn. You will notice that every time you exhale you relax and you are able to twist some more. Breathe lightly when you hold the posture.

CONCENTRATION: Inwardly feel the entire spinal column.

BENEFITS: The benefits of this āsana are incalculable. It strengthens the muscles of the back, and prevents curvature of the spine. In the early stages defects of the spine can be corrected. It prevents and cures lumbago.

On account of unhealthy and unceasing eating habits, the digestive apparatus is kept continually busy by modern man. This implies a great concentration of blood in the abdomen, and with an expansion of the abdominal walls, there is a tendency for idle blood to collect there. Thus the brain is impoverished. This posture gives a gentle squeeze to the abdomen and drives back into useful circulation the idle blood there; it also stimulates the abdominal viscera.

The vagus nerve and the sympathetic nervous system get their twist too, right from their roots (at the neck) down to the solar plexus where the vagus ends, and even below down to the lumbar region. This results in the vitalisation of the several ganglia along the autonomic nervous system and the gradual awakening of the power in it. This power, generated in the supreme 'nerve' centre, viz. the brain, is properly utilized at the different plexuses along the spine and, at the same time, the energy locked up in the abdomen is released for better use. Hence, the yogi is convinced that the technique was revealed by god himself, through one of the greatest divine yogis of India, Matsyendra.

In fact with every posture, as he bends forward and backward, twists and turns, the yogi thanks the lord for the gift of such a marvellous instrument as the body. And it is this remembrance of god which hastens the inner awakening.

36. BE BALANCED: BE SANE
MAYŪRĀSANA

The Bhagavad Gītā describes the yogi as a man of balanced mind. This balance is not a negative, passive state, but something very positive. Balance is the most important thing in our life. If the mind loses its balance, we do the wrong actions, say the wrong words to the wrong person at the wrong time and then go on worrying about them.

The mayūrāsana or the peacock posture looks the very picture of balance. It is not as difficult as it looks; of course you have to be careful, gentle and wise (and is that not the sign of a 'balanced' person?).

The peacock posture or mayūrāsana is possible only if: (a) Sitting erect on the floor you are able to bring the two elbows together and touch the middle of your abdomen with them (keeping your forearms together while doing so). (b) You can bend your wrists back till they are at right angles to the forearm. If these are impossible due to anatomical difficulties, then the peacock posture is not for you.

TECHNIQUE: STAGE ONE: Squat on the ground, sitting on your knees and toes. Bring the forearms together in front of your chest. Partially raise yourself and bring the palms down on the floor in front of you. Now you are standing on 'all fours', with your palms, knees and insteps resting on the floor. The fingers should point towards your knees. If you find that you are not quite comfortable at your wrists, stop here and repeat this step a few times daily for a week or so.

STAGE TWO: Gently, and with intense concentration, lower your abdomen on your elbows, bending the arms at the elbows as much as it is necessary. The forearms should be almost perpendicular to the floor and the elbows as close to the centre of the abdomen as possible. Hold this for a few seconds. Wait. Examine yourself and make sure that you are all right. It may be necessary to readjust the palms slightly to ensure proper balance. Return to the sitting position and do it all over again till you gain mastery over this.

STAGE THREE: Very gently glide forward. If you feel that you are losing your balance and you are inclined to fall, stop the gliding motion and return to the original squatting position. Do it again. Concentrate on the position of the body. You are now standing on your palms and toes. Your aim is to let the whole body rest on the forearms alone. For this you have to find the proper balance. As you glide along, with your abdomen resting on your elbows, you will discover the balance. Very little effort is needed to raise your feet off the floor. Keep your body nearly parallel to the floor.

The Gheraṇḍa Samhitā prescribes the padmāsana position for the legs.

The first impression that you get is 'I cannot do it'. If you are already determined that you cannot do it, how can you? This applies to our life, too. This āsana helps you to overcome lack of confidence.

The second factor in this posture is that having made

up your mind that it is very difficult, you rush through it, as though doing it quickly lessens the difficulty. In fact it only increases it! You will tend to kick and strain; and sure enough, you will fall. That again is true of life.

The third factor is that we should know the laws of balance. Usually the upper part of the body is heavier than the lower and when you lean forward on the elbows using them as a fulcrum, you will find that the legs rise. It is generally more difficult when the forearms are vertical; if you push yourself forward just a little bit you will find that the posture becomes easy. In life too you will have to find out your own balancing point! This āsana brings that truth home to you.

BREATHING: Let the breathing be natural.

The yogi does not neglect the fact that this balance can be achieves only by 'balancing' both the body and mind. He knows that the body is nothing more that the materialisation of the mind. One affects the other. The physical organ that contributes in a big way to the mental balance is the liver, one of the most vital organs in our body. It is this āsana which promotes its well-being.

BENEFITS: The yogi believes that mayurāsana enables you to neutralise and destroy poisons in the body. It also prevents you from becoming unduly fat. It prevents anaemia and also jaundice. It corrects a host of digestive disorders like constipation by exerting a healthy intra-abdominal pressure and giving the whole digestive apparatus a gentle squeeze.

The right elbow presses close to the liver and the left elbow exerts a similar pressure on the spleen, another vitally important organ in our body. Thus mayurāsana achieves a lot for us.

37. YOU CAN BE BEAUTIFUL: IF YOU WANT TO CAKRĀSANA: PĀDAHASTĀSANA: TRIKONĀSANA

Cakrāsana

In order to live a healthy life and enjoy a balanced state of mind and outlook, it is good to ensure that the balancing apparatus in the ears is in a state of health. The yogi achieves it by practise of the cakrāsana (bridge posture).

TECHNIQUE: Lie down on your back. Fold your legs at the knees and draw the feet towards the body, feet just a little apart. Place the palms on the floor just outside the shoulders, with the fingers pointing towards the feet. Inhale, and simultaneously lift your whole body up. Breathe gently and hold for a few seconds to begin with. Use your thought, feeling and awareness to ensure that the pressure on your arms and legs is equal. Gently lower the body and relax. Repeat again a few times.

BENEFITS: This posture closely resembles the dhanurāsana or bow posture. All the good effects of the dhanurāsana are obtained in this posture, too, with the addition of a mild stimulation of the balancing mechanism. The legs and arms are also strengthened by this posture.

Pādahastāsana

In order to ensure harmonious development, the yoga system gives a counterpose for each one. Cakrāsana gives a backward curve; and pādahastāsana gives a forward bend.

TECHNIQUE: Stand erect, with hands raised over the head. Exhale and bend the body forward and down, stretching from the small of the back. Grasp the big toes or place the palms by the side of the feet. Keep the knees stiff and bury the face between the knees. Remain in this posture for a few seconds, and repeat it a few times. The effect of pādahastāsana is the same as paśimottanāsana but with the added advantage that the sudden bending forward stimulates and strengthens the balancing mechanism in the inner ear.

In both cakrāsana and pādhastāsana the blood rushes to the head, helped by the natural force of gravitation. Even those who for some reason or other cannot do the śirasāsana (head stand), will derive some of its benefits from these two postures.

Trikoṇāsana

Trikoṇāsana or triangle posture completes the effect of these two and gives a valuable spinal movement.

TECHNIQUE: Stand upright with the feet three feet apart, arms raised sideways, palms down, parallel to the floor. Let the right foot be turned in and the left turned towards the left. Bend the body to the left, touch the left toes with the left hand, without bending the knees. Bring the right arm parallel to the floor, till the upper arm touches the ear. Keep looking at the right palm. Hold the posture for a few seconds. Repeat with the other side. It is the posture that is important. Let the movement be graceful, in order to remove the very idea of motion from the mind. Yogis insist upon retaining a posture for as long as is possible. Where this is inconvenient, we repeat it, but do not forget that it is retention of the posture that will confer its manifold benefits upon you.

BENEFITS: In trikonasana the spine gets the lateral bending. The abdominal viscera are strengthened and digestive disturbances are remedied.

38. FIRST STEP TO SELF-MASTERY
UḌḌĪYĀNA AND NAULI

Two yoga-practices are combined to promote the vitality of the abdominal organs and also to stir up the latent psychic powers, not with an eye upon their misuse but in order to attain a great measure of self-mastery. These two are uḍḍīyāna and nauli.

They are not easy to learn from books. Here at least it is almost entirely the work of the mind on the body. The more relaxed you are, and the more intense your concentration, the more easily will you get success in these two.

Uḍḍīyāna

TECHNIQUE: Stand with the legs a little apart. Bend slightly forward and place the palms just above the knees. Inhale deeply and exhale fully. As you exhale, concentrate on the abdomen; starting from the lower part of the abdomen, pull the 'inner' contents up – with a backward-upward motion. Hold it for a few seconds. Relax and breathe in.

Nauli

TECHNIQUE: First practise uḍḍīyāna. Isolate the rectus abdonimus and let it drop forward. The two sides of the abdomen look 'hollow' while there is a 'pillar' of the abdominal viscera in the centre. When you can do this with confidence and ease, you can churn the abdomen, clockwise and anticlockwise.

CAUTION: Whereas these are extremely beneficial, any foolish attempt at their violent practise might cause a slight pain in the abdominal muscles and nerves and (some authorities say) such practice is not very good for the heart if there is undue pressure against the diaphragm.

BENEFITS: The benefits are incalculable. The abdominal viscera come under the conscious control of the yogi. Sluggish peristalsis and improper functioning of the vital digestive organs are removed.

Uḍḍīyāna is a bandha (lock). Nauli is a kriyā. Neither is a yoga āsana.

We have come to the end of the essential yoga āsanas.

There are many others, but the ordinary student of yoga may be content with those which we have studied; and they are quite sufficient. We can do all of them within about half an hour and all of them should be done every day.

39. RELAXATION: ŚAVĀSANA

It is highly recommended that between two postures and between two repetitions of the same posture, you should relax for a few seconds and mentally visualise that the energy (prāṇa) that was concentrated in certain parts of the body during the posture, is redistributed throughout the body. Relaxation appears to be most simple, but in truth it is very difficult. Complete relaxation is appropriately called śavāsana (corpse posture).

TECHNIQUE: Start from sitting position, legs in front, knees folded and feet squarely planted on the floor, making sure that your nose is in line with the space between the knees. Gently and uniformly stretch the legs out, making sure that the median line is not disturbed. Let the heels be slightly parted and allow the feet to fall apart.

Place the hands beside you on the floor palms up and roll the back down making sure that you go down vertebra by vertebra and that each part as it comes down sits squarely on the floor. The bridge of the nose should be parallel to the ceiling, and the chin at right angles.

Adjust the shoulders so that the shoulder blades are flat on the floor. Rest the fingertips on shoulders and allow elbows to fall at a comfortable angle from the body. Allow the forearms to fall gently to the floor (palms up).

Focus the eyes on the region of the heart, to relax the eyelids and the eyes. Listen to your own breathing.

Take a deep breath and suddenly 'let go'. Let the whole of the weight of your body and thoughts drop away completely. Mentally go down to and catch hold of your toes. To make sure you have done so, tense the toes. Then relax. This tension-relaxation is like self-massage and can be done in three stages. First produce a mild tension-relaxation. Next time let it be a little firmer. Lastly, let it be 'sudden' and intense. The last relaxation is complete relaxation and conscious relaxation too. Now shift the attention to the calf muscles; follow the same procedure. Go up in this manner part by part of the body till you reach the chest. Then the hands and up to the shoulders. Continue with the neck, mouth, eyes, eyebrows, forehead. Each time you have relaxed a part of the body become aware of the vibrations of prāṇa in that area, and actually visualise that all the organs there are completely relaxed.

Yājñavalkya gives the following sixteen parts from which to withdraw the mind step by step. We can adopt this list for our relaxation: great toes; ankles; middle of shanks; part above the shanks and below knees; centre of knees; centre of thighs; from thighs to navel; navel; heart; the right arm; the left arm; pit of the throat; roof of the palate; root of the nose; eyeballs; centre of eyebrows; forehead; crown of head.

Now relax the brain, too: the best way to do this is to offer a prayer to god. Feel that you are floating in a cloud of grace, free from all pains, cares and anxieties, resting in the lap of god. Feel that his grace and his light flow into you and fill your brain, and flow to all parts of your body, filling them with health, well-being and vitality. Gently roll the head from side to side; stretch the hands and feet. Gently open your eyes and gently get up.

After a vigorous practice of the yoga āsanas there is perfect relaxation. In perfect relaxation the intelligence that rules the body is free from interference. It is clear, light and luminous and in that light you see that the state of relaxation is not lethargy, and that it is possible to be relaxed even in the midst of the intensest activity.

The alternating tensing and relaxing will be more effective if you synchronise inhalation with 'tense' and exhalation with 'relax'.

40. *THE INCREDIBLE SECRET: PRĀṆA*

The pace and the texture of modern life have become so fast and so complex that we simply refuse to believe in the simple. Thus, when the yogi offers us the secret of life – that with the help of the life-breath we can achieve relaxation, clarity of intellect and emotional stability, we think that it is incredible and impossible.

Thousands of years ago the yogi discovered that breath has an intimate connection with thoughts and emotions. The great sage Vasiṣṭha in his celebrated teaching known as Yoga Vasiṣṭha says:

"In this body, that energy which circulates in the energy channels (nāḍīs) is known as prāṇa. In accordance with its diverse functions in the body, it is also known by the names of āpana, etc. This prāṇa is indistinguishably united with the mind. In fact, the consciousness that tends towards thinking on account of the movement of prāṇa is known as the mind. Movement of thought in the mind arises from the movement of prāṇa; and movement of prāṇa arises because of the movement of thought in consciousness. They thus form a cycle of mutual dependence like waves and movement of currents in water. The wise ones declare that the mind is caused by the movement of prāṇa; and hence by the restraint of the prāṇa the mind becomes quiescent."

(Upaśanti Prakaraṇaṁ, chapter 78)

When our thoughts are concentrated and our emotions are well under control, the breath is calm, deep and rhythmic. On the other hand, when the thoughts and emotions are in a state of imbalance, as when we are excited or in a state of anger, the breath is uneven, fast and disturbed.

If the emotional upset was accompanied by disturbed breathing, regulated breathing will naturally be accompanied by balanced thinking and emotional stability. This is the yogi's simple logic, proven axiom and incredible secret. In fact, it may well be that breathing in and out does not have the ventilation of the lungs and the oxygenation of the blood as its only or even main purposes.

All this could have been achieved by merely keeping the lungs open, even as a room is open to outside air which therefore circulates freely in the room without the walls having to inhale and exhale. Maharishi Patanjali in his Yoga Sutras also suggests that inhalation and exhalation indicate the degree of mental distraction (chapter 1. sutra 31). Ramana Maharishi considered watching or listening to the breath itself as prāṇāyāma. Prāṇāyāma is not ' restraint of the life-force' but ' the realisation of the life-force' .

There are numerous theories concerning this prāṇa, but the theories themselves are not prāṇa. We cannot see the prāṇa; it is the prāṇa that enables us to see. Prāṇa is not the object of thought but its subject; thought moves because of prāṇa. It is life, though not as we understand it. It presides over even what we call death. In life it performs a myriad of functions to help the body function; in death it patiently decomposes the body so that the elements may return to their source; and it is this prāṇa that lives in all beings, as all things. It is everything, whatever moves (in which it is the kinetic energy) and what does not move (in which it is static energy).

It is the cosmic power or energy. It is also known as citti śakti or kuṇḍalinī śakti. When this energy is 'asleep' there is a cloud of ignorance which veils self-knowledge. Prāṇāyāma is essentially a way to awaken this sleeping energy and thus to dispel this cloud of ignorance.

41. POSTURES FOR PRĀṆĀYĀMA AND MEDITATION

The haṭha yoga scriptures contain descriptions of the following postures especially suited to the practice of both prāṇāyāma and meditation.

Siddhāsana

Siddhāsana, or the posture of the adept, is regarded as the best among the meditative postures.

TECHNIQUE: Press the perineum with the left heel. Place the right heel on the pubic region. The toes of one foot are then locked in between the thigh and the calf muscle of the other leg. Drop the chin on the chest and make a firm chin-lock. Keep the back quite straight. Gaze steadily at the space between the eyebrows.

Padmāsana

Padmāsana, or the lotus posture, is of course the most popular among the practitioners of yoga.

TECHNIQUE: Place the right foot on the left thigh and the left foot on the right thigh. The soles face up. Let the hands rest on the lap, palms facing upwards, one on top of the other. Rest the tip of the tongue at the roof of the front teeth. Form the chin-lock. Gaze at the eyebrow centre.

BENEFITS: In this posture the yogi endeavours to unite the apāṇa with the prāṇa and thus to awaken the kuṇḍalinī. Hence, the scriptures declare that this posture destroys all ailments.

Bhadrāsana

TECHNIQUE: Place the right heel on the right side of the perineum and the left heel on the left side, with the soles of the feet in contact with each other. Now hold the feet firmly. Keep the body erect. The gaze is directed at the eyebrow centre and the chin is firmly pressed on the chest.

BENEFITS: The same as for other meditative postures.

Svastikāsana

TECHNIQUE: Fold the legs at the knees. Insert the right foot between the left thigh and calf and the left foot between the right thigh and calf. Keep the body straight. This is the posture of peace and auspiciousness.

Gomukhāsana

TECHNIQUE: Cross the ankles under the body so that the right heel is under the left buttock and the left heel is under the right buttock. The heels can be beside the respective buttocks. Let the hands rest on the right knee. This posture resembles the face of a cow. It is suitable for meditation.

Vīrāsana

TECHNIQUE: 'Place one foot on the other thigh. Later, use the other foot similarly.' The technique seems to indicate the half-lotus posture. Some yogis say that this can be done sitting on a raised seat: the left foot is placed on the floor and the right foot rests on the left thigh.

Vajrāsana

TECHNIQUE: Sit on the heels or between the heels. Keep the hands on the knees and the back straight. Do the chin-lock and gaze at the eyebrow centre.

BENEFITS: This is also a good meditation posture. Our master Swami Sivananda recommended that we should sit in this posture for a few minutes after meals – it improves digestion.

Sukhāsana

TECHNIQUE: Any comfortable sitting posture is sukhāsana. This is what the word means.

42. *REALISATION OF THE LIFE-FORCE*
PRĀṆĀYĀMA

To breathe correctly looks simple on the face of it, but when we sit down to do it we realise that we have forgotten how to breathe properly, and we begin to wonder how we live. We have forgotten the utter simplicity of total breathing.

Many people have cultivated the habit of drawing the abdomen in while breathing in, contrary to the natural way of allowing the diaphragm to drop, thus pushing the abdominal walls slightly out in front. This must be corrected, to begin with.

Try this: Hold the palms a fraction of an inch in front of your abdomen, palms facing the body. Take a deep breath till the abdomen actually pushes the palms away. Exhale, at the same time pressing the abdomen in firmly with your palms. Do this with deep concentration so that you get the right inner feeling, after which you may dispense with the ceremony of holding the palms in front of the abdomen. (Some people find it more effective to begin with an exhalation with the palms pressing the abdomen in.) Repeat this thrice.

The next step: Hold the sides of the rib cage with your palms. Exhale and press the palms inwards; inhale and let the rib cage expand and push the palms away. Do this thrice.

The third step: Fold the arms sideways and gently grip your shoulders with your fingers, your elbows are now spread out as your wings. Still gripping the shoulders, raise your elbows till they point upwards, at the same time inhaling deeply. Gently lower the elbows to the previous position, exhaling. Do this thrice.

These three together enable you to get the feeling of parts of a complete breath. Please do not use this as a ritual; it is only meant to give you the feeling of a complete breath, which is combining the three steps given above into one long smooth wavelike movement. As you start to inhale, allow the incoming air to push the abdomen forward for a second or two; then, still inhaling, allow it to drop back as the rib cage expands sideways; finally bring the air to the top of the chest. Then, exhaling, let the rib cage move back, finally drawing the abdomen in as you exhale completely. As long as you are trying to do this, you are not doing it correctly! But, hopefully, you will suddenly discover this one of these days and then you will breathe like a baby without creating a division (between the abdomen, the rib cage and the top) where no division exists!

Now try the following exercises before going on to the prāṇāyāma of haṭha yoga:

(1) Be seated comfortably on a straight-backed chair, with your feet planted squarely on the floor, chin up and the whole back straight but not stiff. This posture is the second best if you cannot sit in padmāsana or the lotus posture. If you rock with your body very gently forward and backward you can discover your own centre of gravity where there is an inward feeling of weightlessness. Close your eyes if there are distractions; otherwise keep them open, softly gazing at a point about two feet in front of you. Watch your own breath. Listen to it, without deliberately producing any sound or regulating the breath. (Incidentally this is the easiest way to relax any tension.) Breathe slowly in and out with both the nostrils. See that there are no jerks while inhaling or exhaling. Breathe more and more deeply, slightly heaving the chest and even bulging the abdomen outward, but with the minimum effort. Occasionally you may let the breath produce a mild sound as in the ujjāyi prāṇāyāma or even the bhramarī prāṇāyāma (to be described later in this section); that will enable you to ensure that the breathing in and out is smooth

(2) Still using both the nostrils simultaneously, breathe in and hold the breath within for a few seconds each time, and then breathe out. Be sure that this does not result in a forced or hurried exhalation. Breathing must still be even and graceful. Do this for a fortnight or a month before attempting to regulate the breath. Try to work toward the ratio of 1:4:2, i.e., one unit for inhalation, four for retention and two for exhalation.

(3) Still using both the nostrils simultaneously, become aware of the sensation of the inner holding of the breath at the following points: (i) at the tip of the nose – in order to do this, you will have to block the tips of the nostrils with the fingers and then blow the breath out; (ii) at the junction of the nostrils with the throat – to do so you lift up the root of the tongue; (iii) at the base of the

throat – open the mouth just a little to get this sensation; (iv) in the middle of the chest and (v) at the solar plexus. In the last two cases you may have to exhale the air a little after the completion of the inhalation to ensure that there is no block except where it is desired.

(4) In this exercise the inhalation and exhalation can be with both nostrils together. Inhale slowly through both nostrils. Watch the breathing and remain constantly aware of the breath flowing in through the nostrils. Keep inhaling even when you 'think' this flow has stopped. Watch for the moment when this inhalation *has to change* to exhalation. During this period the 'impulse to inhale' is sustained. The breath is obviously held within, and the whole chest is 'open' in terms of exercise (3.v). When exhalation commences let it similarly proceed slowly till all the air has been exhaled. At the same time draw the adbomen in. Keep up the impulse to exhale as long as is possible. Now there is 'external kumbhaka'. Watch for the 'moment of change' when exhalation naturally comes to an end and inhalation has to commence. It is a beautiful exercise which combines internal kumbhaka and external kumbhaka as also awareness of breathing. There should be no strain in this practice.

(5) When the previous exercise becomes easy and natural, then you may attempt alternate nostril breathing. Use the fingers of the right hand to close the nostrils. The thumb closes the right nostril; the ring and the little fingers close the left nostril. The other two fingers are usually folded on the palm, but some prefer to let them rest on the space between the eyebrows. It is better not to remove the fingers entirely from the wings of the nostril even when the particular nostril is open.

Inhale through the left nostril (the Haṭha Yoga Pradīpikā commences the prāṇāyāma with the left nostril). Exhale through the right. Inhale through the right. Exhale through the left. Without holding the breath, try to prolong the inhalation and exhalation. Ensure that the breathing is smooth and graceful. Watch the breath carefully. See if you can become aware of the exact moment at which inhalation turns into exhalation and exhalation into inhalation.

(6) If the alternate nostril breathing is easy, smooth and graceful, hold the breath after the inhalation. Become aware of the point at which the breathing is held, which should be at least 'in

the middle of the chest' mentioned in paragraph (3) above. This is also the purpose of the chin-lock which is recommended by most yogis. If this is not done, then the breath knocks at the throat and creates discomfort. It is good to let the breathing work out the right ratio without conscious effort or use of the will. This is what our master Swami Sivananda called sukha pūrvaka prāṇāyāma – easy comfortable prāṇāyāma.

(7) During the same alternate nostril breathing, split the inhalation into three instalments with a three second interval between instalments. The exhalation is smooth and continuous, after the usual retention of the breath. After a few rounds of this, let the inhalation be continuous and the exhalation be broken up into three instalments with a three-second interval between instalments. Watch to see at which point the breath is held. A great yogi Satchidananda Paramahansa highly recommends this practice which prevents the breathing from becoming mechanical.

(8) Again, with the same alternate nostril breathing technique given in paragraph (6) above, try to hold the lungs empty for a few seconds after every exhalation and before commencing the next inhalation through the same nostril through which the exhalation was done. The uḍḍīyāna bandha happens: and if it does, it is effective. If you hold the lungs empty for longer than your capacity warrants, your next inhalation will be violent; it is good to avoid this, without unduly shortening the period of retention.

If you devote half an hour in the morning and half an hour in the evening to the practice of these exercises, you will discover that not only are you immediately relieved of any nervous tension (and intellectual and emotional imbalance) but your normal breathing habit is soon changed for the better. You will not get exhausted as often and as much as before and you will face life itself more calmly, hopefully and cheerfully.

A few hints concerning these practices may be useful at this stage.

When you practise the alternate nostril breathing and use the right hand for this purpose, it is advisable in the beginning to practise in front of a mirror or a monitor to ensure that you are still sitting straight and that your face is not turned towards the right and the body is not leaning to the right.

One wonders why all this fuss, when both the nostrils lead to one throat. The inspired air has not only the oxygen our blood needs, but something very subtle which even the nerve-endings in the nostrils can absorb. The nerve-endings in the left nostril differ in their 'polarity' from those in the right nostril; even as a single piece of magnet has two different poles at the two ends. The right nostril is considered solar, positive and warm, and the left is considered lunar, negative and cool.

The arm that is used in this practice might experience discomfort if it is held up for a considerable time. You may use the other arm, alternately. Or use a coffee table or the T-shaped yoga-daṇḍa (yoga stick) which the yogis use to support the arm.

Why the ratio 1:4:2? It is interesting. Modern physiology claims that of the oxygen we breathe in we use only about one-fifth and breathe out the rest of it. What a waste! The yogi by retaining the breath for the four units, ensures the maximum use of the inhaled air.

What does unit 1 represent? The Yoga-cintāmaṇi says that it is the time taken for one breath during sleep. But Yājñavalkya says that circling the knee thrice with the hand (neither fast nor slow) and then snapping the fingers, is the duration of one unit. The latter is the generally accepted scale.

43. THE HEART OF HAṬHA YOGA KUMBHAKA

Relaxation, release from tension and the ability to live a happy and healthy life are incidental to the principal aim of hatha yoga, which is self-knowledge. Meditation is the means to self-knowledge, and quiescence of the mind is necessary for meditation. Prāṇāyāma is practised for reaching this quiescence of the mind. The very essence of prāṇāyāma is the kumbhaka or the retention (or suspension) of breathing.

When the Gheraṇḍa Saṁhitā enumerates a variety of prāṇāyāmas it calls them kumbhakas. Eight such kumbhakas are described: sahita, sūryabheda, ujjāyī, śītāli, bhastrikā, bhrāmarī, mūrcchā and kevalī. Just as āsana means posture and holding the posture is its vital essence, kumbhaka means suspension of breath and that is its vital part, even though the inhalations and exhalations may also be elaborated.

Both the Haṭha Yoga Pradīpikā and the Gheraṇḍa Saṁhitā demand that the practitioner should ensure that the nādīs are clear before embarking upon a serious practice of these kumbhakas. The six cleansing processes have already been described: the special mystic purification prāṇāyāma as laid down in the Gheraṇḍa Saṁhitā will be described in the chapter on laya yoga.

The technique of the kumbhakas is given below:

Sahita

This kumbhaka can be practised in two ways: with or without the repetition of certain mantras.

Sit in any comfortable posture. Contemplate Brahma the creator who is of a red colour. Inhale by the left nostril, mentally repeating the sound 'a' for the duration of sixteen units. After the inhalation and before the kumbhaka, do the uḍḍīyāna by pulling the abdomen up. While doing the kumbhaka, contemplate Vishnu who is dark in colour, at the same time mentally repeat the sound 'u' for the duration of sixty-four units. Exhale through the right nostril similarly contemplating Śiva who is of a white colour and mentally repeating the sound 'm' for the duration of thirty-two units. Then inhale through the right, hold the breath as before, and exhale through the left.

It is recommended after the inhalation that the chin-lock is done and that during the exhalation the uḍḍīyāna bandha is done. Towards the close of the exhalation, and therefore during the next inhalation, the mūlabandha is practised. By this the prāṇa is forced into the central channel or the suṣumṇā. The prāṇa is pushed down by the chin-lock and apāna pulled up by the mūlabandha.

The word sahita means 'with' as distinct from kevala which means 'alone' i.e. without. The allusion is to the inhalation and the exhalation. In sahita there are inhalation and exhalation; in kevala there is retention alone.

The sahita kumbhaka is the mainstay of the prāṇāyāma practice. It is classified into the best, the middling and the inferior on the basis of the length of the kumbhaka. The ratio of 20:80:40 units is the best; 16:64:32 is the middling; and 12:48:24 is the inferior.

The texts mention that the practice of this kumbhaka may be accompanied by the following symptoms:

The inferior type (the beginner) experiences profuse perspiration. (The perspiration that issues during the prāṇāyāma should not be wiped but rubbed into the body; otherwise there is loss of energy.) The middling type experiences tremors of the body. The best type of practitioner, who is surely advanced in his practice, experiences the entry of prāṇa into the suṣuṁnā-nādī.

The Lingapurāṇaṁ and Gorakṣa give different ratios for the middling and the best type of practitioner. 24:96:48 is the middling and 36:144:72 is the best. They also declare that in the best type of kumbhaka the mind is stilled into a state of unconsciousness of the external world, the prāṇa unites with the apāna and enters the suṣuṃna-nāḍī.

The Haṭha Yoga Pradīpikā declares that one should practise prāṇāyāma four times every day (at sunrise, midday, sunset and midnight), gradually increasing the number of kumbhakas till one is able to do eighty kumbhakas at each of the four sittings. The Kūrmapurāṇaṁ recommends that the student should do ten kumbhakas on the first day and increase the number by five daily (or weekly). The Pradīpikā prescribes the sahita prāṇāyāma for the purification of the nādīs and declares that one who practises it thus achieves purification of the nādīs in three months.

The Gheraṇḍa Saṁhitā promises peace of mind, psychic powers, bliss and the awakening of the kuṇḍalinī śakti as the fruits of the above kumbhaka.

Sūryabheda

TECHNIQUE: Sit in a comfortable posture. Inhale through the right nostril. Do the chin-lock (jālandhara bandha). Hold the breath till the breath (prāṇa) enters every cell of your body from the top of the head to the tip of the toes and perspiration pours from every pore of the body. Then slowly exhale through the left nostril, at the same time doing the uḍḍīyāna bandha. Towards the conclusion mūlabandha is practised.

Such retention of breath is the rule in the case of the other prāṇāyāmas that follow. The coward reading the description is frightened away; the serious student discovers during the practice that there is no danger at all in it. Prāṇa or the life-force is beyond the 'me' or the ego-sense. Your own limit for the retention of breath is set by this prāṇa! This discovery makes the student fearless. He learns to trust the divine intelligence beyond the ego-principle and surrender the ego itself to it. Needless to say, the presence of an expert guru enables the student to overcome the irrational fear.

Ujjāyī

TECHNIQUE: The Haṭha Yoga Pradīpikā has a simple technique. Slowly inhale with both nostrils while partially closing the glottis so that there is a resonance from the throat to the chest. Practise kumbhaka or retention as before. Exhale through the left nostril. This can be done even while walking or standing, obviously without the prolonged kumbhaka.

The Gheraṇḍa Saṁhitā description differs considerably – but it is interesting. Inhale with both nostrils; while doing so keep your mouth shut but drop the gullet inwardly as if you are about to yawn with closed mouth. Now the inhaled air fills your mouth, too. At the same time close the glottis and produce a sound as in the previous technique. At the conclusion of the inhalation swallow the air you hold in your mouth. Then do the kumbhaka as before, with the chin-lock. Exhale.

BENEFITS: "Practise ujjāyī to overcome old age and death," says Gheraṇḍa Saṁhitā (which also says that it is a cure for consumption, fever and dysentery).

Śītāli

TECHNIQUE: Inhale through the tongue (rolled into a tube and slightly protruding from the mouth). Do kumbhaka as before. Exhale through the nose. (Śītāli means 'cooling').

BENEFITS: It cures biliousness. Gheraṇḍa calls it the giver of bliss.

Bhastrikā

TECHNIQUE: Bhastrikā means bellows. Here the abdomen is used like a bellows. Haṭha Yoga Pradīpikā commences the bhastrikā with a rapid exhalation 'till it resounds the heart, throat and head.' Inhale similarly till the chest is filled. Again exhale rapidly and powerfully; and inhale. Repeat this twenty times. Inhale through the right nostril after the last rapid exhalation. Hold the nostrils tight and practise kumbhaka as before. Exhale through the left. (Our master encouraged the use of both nostrils for the final inhalation and exhalation.)

BENEFITS: It makes the prāṇa flow through the suṣuṁnā-nāḍī. Gheraṇḍa asks the student to do this thrice and assures that thus he will never suffer from any disease.

Bhrāmarī

TECHNIQUE: Close the eyes and listen to the inner sounds. Gheraṇḍa recommends that this be practised at midnight in a place where there is no noise.

The Haṭha Yoga Pradīpikā has a different approach: Inhale rapidly making the sound of a male-bee. Practise kumbhaka as usual. Exhale slowly making the sound of a female-bee. (Bhrāmarī means 'bee'.)

BENEFITS: It is a great aid to concentration of the mind.

Mūrcchā

TECHNIQUE: Inhale through the nostrils. Press the chin firmly against the chest (jālandhara bandha). After kumbhaka, exhale very slowly while concentrating on the eyebrow centre. This is according to the Haṭha Yoga Pradīpikā. Gheraṇḍa, however, says that when this kumbhaka is performed with the mind concentrated on the eyebrow centre, fainting will result – as also the experience of bliss. (Mūrcchā means 'fainting'.)

Kevalī

TECHNIQUE: Gheraṇḍa prescribes intense concentration of the mind on the so-haṁ sound of the breathing ('so' in inhalation and 'haṁ' in the exhalation). When this concentration is perfect, the breath 'remains within the body. There is suspension of breathing, without inhalation and exhalation. (Sohaṁ is a mantra which means 'That I am'.)

Sitkārī

The Haṭha Yoga Pradīpikā omits the sahita kumbhaka (which is the simple prāṇāyāma anyway) and kevalī kumbhaka (which is treated as the culmination of the practice and not as a special exercise). Instead it mentions sitkārī and plāvīni.

TECHNIQUE: Inhale through the mouth, making a hissing sound. Practise kumbhaka as usual. Exhale through the nostrils.

BENEFITS: It drives away lethargy.

Plāvīni

TECHNIQUE: Drink air as you drink water, and fill the stomach with it. Retain it for some time and expel it.

BENEFITS: It enables you to float on water.

44. GENERAL ADVICE

For the guidance of those who wish to take up the practice of yoga seriously, the Haṭha Yoga Pradīpikā and the Gheraṇḍa Saṁhitā provide a few rules:

The student should practise yoga in a modest hermitage which is situated in a peaceful environment. The hermitage itself should have a small door and no other opening. It should not be long or it may distract one's attention. It should be clean.

(Jñāneśvara in his celebrated commentary on the Bhagavad Gītā says that the place chosen should be one that is frequented by holy men and it should have a natural spiritual atmosphere so that (a) one who goes there would wish to practise yoga and (b) "Should a heretic enter the place unawares, even he would feel a strong inclination to practise penance.")

It is best to commence the practice of yoga during either the spring or the autumn.

The yogi should observe strict moderation in eating. The Gheraṇḍa Saṁhitā says: "Pure, sweet and cooling food should be eaten to fill half the stomach; one quarter of the stomach should be filled with water; one quarter should be kept for the movement of air."

The Saṁhitā also prohibits bath in the early morning, any observance that causes physical discomfort, like fasting or living on one meal a day.

The Haṭha Yoga Pradīpikā lists the following as the causes for failure in yoga: "Overeating, too much of exertion, excessive talk, the observance of dull routines, bad company and unsteadiness." It also suggests these six aids: "Zeal, determination, courage, right knowledge, steadfastness, and the avoidance of contact with people."

Another text of yoga known as Yogānuśāsanam has the following list of aids and obstacles: 'Success in yoga is impossible for one who has no faith and who does not exert, who is attached, who is devoid of keenness, who is not devoted to the guru, who is given to falsehood and harsh and arrogant speech.' The following six are the aids: 'Confidence in one's yoga practice, intense faith, devotion to the guru, a state of equilibrium, control of the senses and moderation in eating – there is no need for a seventh aid!' However, the scripture recommends the cultivation of dispassion, listening to philosophical discourses, singing the Lord's names, listening to good music and cultivation of virtues.

In the beginning of the practice of prāṇāyāma the student would do well to take a little milk before commencing. After the conclusion of the practice, he should have a hot bath.

During the entire practice, and especially during the kumbhaka, he should repeat his own mantra; this was our master's special advice.

The scriptures even suggest the following procedure: Wake up at dawn or at sunrise. Adore the guru at the crown of the head and the lord in the heart. Attend to the ablutions and cleaning of the teeth, etc. Sit down on a soft seat. Meditate on the guru and god. Practise some āsanas (savāsana only, if you are tired) and also viparītakaranī (or śirasāsana) before commencing prāṇāyāma. Viparītakaranī and śirasāsana should be avoided during the evening and night practice.

The Kūrmapurānaṁ suggests the following sequence: Commence with the sukha-purvaka prāṇāyāma (the alternate nostril breathing) with kumbhaka. Then sūryabhedanaṁ, ujjāyī, sītkārī, śītalī and bhastrikā in that order. Then others. Conclude with contemplation on the inner sound (nāḍa-cintanaṁ).

The Gheraṇḍa Saṁhitā asks the yogi to sit facing the east or the north; east is where the sun rises, and north is the field of positive magnetic activity.

What should the yogi sit on for his yoga-practice? The Bhagavad Gīta prescribes a seat of kuśa-grass with a deer-skin on top of it and a piece of cloth on top of that. The Gheraṇḍa Saṁhitā says that the yogi "should sit on a seat of kuśa-grass or a deer-skin or tiger-skin or a blanket or on earth."

Prāṇāyāma is not mere rhythmic breathing as it is commonly misunderstood. It is exercise or extension of the life-force (prāṇa) which uses the body and mind, and which is used by them. This intimate connection should be clearly grasped. Prāṇa and the body together enable us to live. With all this yoga-practice and prāṇāyāma, if our life is not well regulated and if we waste our life-force in a hundred ways, it is idle to expect to make any progress in any direction. Yet, if our life is regulated and at the same time we practise yoga āsanas and prāṇāyāma, they will lead us to the next step —meditation — and ultimately to god, the supreme bliss.

45. WHAT SHALL I EAT?

Dietetic discipline is part of this overall discipline of yoga. The body is made of the food that you eat. Therefore, your health depends to a large extent on the food that you consume.

The yogi goes a step further and says that the subtlest portion of the food builds your mind. It 'colours the mind' might perhaps be a better expression, nearer the truth. Hence the yogi is extremely selective in his food.

My guru Swami Sivananda used to say that a diet of fruits and milk is most conducive to a meditative mood and is therefore the ideal food for the serious student of yoga. In his book on yoga āsanas, haṭha yoga and so on, Swami Sivananda has given detailed lists of articles of food which are recommended and others which are forbidden for the student of yoga.

Coarse food makes our mind coarse, unfit to pursue the refined and delicate task of meditation. I have seen this myself in the Himalayas: a monkey when it feeds on cooked and spiced food is aggressive and hostile, whereas when the same monkey lives on leaves and fruits it is calm, non-violent and introvert. Denatured food deprives us of our good nature.

What about meat eating? Meat is entirely unnecessary. A totally vegetarian diet is infinitely better than a diet of meat. Medical science agrees. Here is an excerpt from 'The British Medical Journal':–

"Epidemiological studies of heart disease suggest that some at least of the deaths in middle age from myocardial infarction could be cut by a move towards a more prudent diet – which means more cereals and vegetables and less meat and fat."

A vegetarian diet has also been found to be more economical at both the domestic and the national levels.

"But, from where do you get animal protein so very essential for the building of your tissues?" asks a friend. The reply is simple: "The body produces its own protein, just as the body of the herbivorous animal does, whose flesh you eat!" People eat only herbivorous animals. Their flesh is nothing but secondhand vegetable. Why not eat fresh vegetable, instead?

All the above is apart from the ethical principles involved, the highest of which is 'ahiṁsā' (non-violence). Even if you do not directly engage in the act of killing the animals, you participate in their murder by providing the market for the criminal. If you have not developed the sensitivity to spare the animal's life by refusing to eat its flesh, how can you hope to attain cosmic consciousness which is the consciousness of the oneness of all beings?

Of course, even vegetables have rudimentary life. However, in nature there is a reciprocal relationship between the plant and the animals (including human beings); whatever we give the plant takes and whatever it gives we consume.

It is possible for even habitual meat-eaters to give up the bad habit, if they want to, by initially cutting meat out on one day (on Friday) a week and then extending this to cover the whole week.

In regard to other types of food, adopt the motto of moderation. Eat as little as you really need. This will preserve the digestive organs in excellent shape.

The sincere student of yoga will, of course, never touch alcohol and tobacco; and will progressively try to avoid all stimulants and unnatural food and drink.

Eat good food in a good mood. The mood is very important. The mood of the giver of the food is as important as that of the receiver. The yogi offers all food to the deity and takes it as sacrament, as god's gift to him. One who serves food to another treats the latter as god.

46. THE SEAL OF TRIUMPH MUDRĀ

The Haṭha Yoga Pradīpikā recommends the practice of the mudrā after prāṇāyāma: some yogis prefer to practise some or all the mudrās after the āsanas and before prāṇāyāma.

Mudrā is a seal both in the sense of the seal of authority and the seal that closes and safeguards. The Pradīpikā describes ten mudrās, while Gheraṇḍa Saṁhitā speaks of twenty-five. In both the lists are included what are known as bandhas, the meaning and the effect being the same as those for the mudrās. The purpose of the mudrās is said to be the awakening of the kuṇḍalinī śakti.

Yoga Mudrā

TECHNIQUE: Sit in Padmāsana. Hold the toes. Or, hold the left wrist with the right hand, behind the back. Softly exhaling, bend forward and touch the ground with your face. Breathe normally. Concentrate on the spinal column.

Mahāmudrā

TECHNIQUE: Press the perineum with the left heel. Keep the right leg stretched in front, making sure that it is at a right-angle to the body. Take hold of the right foot with both hands. Inhale. Drop the chin and press it firmly against the chest. Inwardly raise the prāṇa up. Turn the gaze towards the eyebrow centre. After holding the breath to your capacity, release the chin-lock and exhale very slowly. Repeat it using the other leg. Do this several times on each side.

This should be immediately followed by the

Mahābandha

TECHNIQUE: Press the perineum with the left heel, Place the right foot on the left thigh. Inhale. Do the chin-lock as before. Practise mulabandha (page 102) also. Meditate on the susumna-nadi. Hold the breath to your capacity. Exhale slowly. Repeat it on the other side, using the other leg.

The Gheraṇḍa Saṁhitā recommends moving the rectum in addition to the practice of the mūlabandha, to make it more effective.

An alternative to the chin-lock (jālandhara bandha) is also suggested: press the tip of the tongue against the front teeth (jihvā-bandha). This has the same effect.

This again should be immediately followed by the:

Mahāvedha

TECHNIQUE: Begin with the mahābandha posture. Inhale. Make the chin-lock. Hold the breath. Place the palms on the floor. Lift the whole body up and gently strike the floor with the body. Prāṇa and the apāna unite by this and the vital force enters the suṣuṁnā nāḍī or the central channel. The Haṭha Yoga Pradīpikā states, "There is a death-like state; then the air should be exhaled."

The Pradīpikā recommends that these three should together be practised by a serious student of yoga every three hours!

Khecarī Mudrā

TECHNIQUE: When the tongue enters the posterior nares and the gaze is fixed between the eyebrows, it is khecarī. This is achieved by systematically cutting the frenum linguae, lengthening the tongue till one is able to touch the forehead with its tip. All the haṭha yoga texts sing the glory of this mudrā and unanimously declare that when the tongue points upwards the yogi drinks nectar, he is freed from old age and death, and he easily enters into samādhi. It is said that khecarī should be practised till yoga-nidrā is experienced – which is when the mind is absorbed in the centre between the eyebrows.

Some yogis believe that this is similar to what the hibernating animals do.

The Yoga Vāsiṣṭha suggests that for this purpose it is sufficient if the tip of the tongue touches the uvula. The late Paramahaṃsa Satchidānanda Yogiśvara was also of that opinion: he declared that when the tip of the tongue is thus turned up and back, mental agitation ceases.

The Gheraṇḍa Saṁhitā describes a similar practice known as nabho-mudrā, "Wherever he is and in whatever work the yogi is engaged, he should turn the tongue up and hold the breath."

(Khecarī means 'moving in space'. The khecarī mudrā is reputed to confer upon the practitioner the power to roam at will in space. In some tāntrik texts khecarī means 'air which moves in space', and kumbhaka or holding the breath is referred to as khecarī-bandhaṇaṁ.) Khecarī mudrā in this sense may refer to kumbhaka.

Uḍḍīyana bandha

The technique has already been described on page 79.

Mūlabandha

TECHNIQUE: Press the left heel against the perineum. Contract the rectum and inwardly pull the rectum and the perineum up. Draw the abdomen back towards the spine. The Gheraṇḍa Samhitā adds: "Place the right heel on the pubic region (which makes it the siddhāsana also)." This is a very important practice in connection with prāṇāyāma, as also the awakening of the kuṇḍalinī śakti. Through this practice the prāṇa and the apāna are brought together; they easily enter the suṣuṁnā-nāḍī. Great energy and heat are generated by this practice.

Jālandhara bandha

TECHNIQUE: Drop the head forward. Press the chin firmly against the chest, thus squeezing the throat.

BENEFITS: This ties up the network (jāla) of the nāḍīs and thus prevents the downward flow of the nectar from its source above the palate. Thus the nectar is saved from being consumed by the gastric fire.

When the yogi practises the three bandhas together – the mūlabandha (contracting the rectum and the perineum), jālandhara bandha (contracting the neck) and the uḍḍīyāna bandha (contracting the abdomen) – prāṇa and apāna unite and enter into the suṣuṁnā-nāḍī. The prāṇa is no longer agitated. It is steady. This is bandha-traya (triple lock).

Viparītakaraṇī

The description is vague enough to suggest the half shoulder-stand (sarvāṅgāsana) and the head-stand (śirasāsana). The Pradīpikā says that this increases the gastric fire and the yogi should not go hungry.

Vajroli

When one is able to arrest the flow of the seminal fluid and retrieve it even when it has been discharged, it is vajroli. This is according to the Pradīpikā, which also calls it yoni mudrā.

The Gheraṇḍa Saṁhitā, however, describes it differently: "Place the palms on the ground and raise the legs up in the air, the head not touching the earth."

Śakticālanaṁ

TECHNIQUE: It should be remembered that this is a technique for forcing the kuṇḍalinī-śakti to move. Inhale through the right nostril and exhale through the left after a brief retention. Then practise the abdominal movement which resembles but is not exactly nauli kriyā. If this is done for a long time, it is good to practise the simple (inhale-hold-exhale) prāṇāyāma every few minutes. It will enhance the śakticālana effect. After this be seated in siddhāsana (the Pradīpikā calls this the vajrāsana also). Grasp the ankles and exert pressure on the kanda which lies just above the peri neum. Practise bhastrikā kumbhaka.

The kuṇḍalinī which has already been moved by the previous practice now awakens. The third part of this technique is: contract the solar plexus repeatedly. This is done by agnisara (see Laya Yoga). By these three practices the kuṇḍalinī begins to move in the suṣumṇānāḍī. Needless to say, this practice is meant only for one whose life is totally dedicated to the practice of haṭha yoga. Such a person is probably living with a teacher. Even if you are living with an expert teacher, you will still have to be guided by your inner guru, commonsense.

BENEFITS: The text assures that "One who observes moderation in eating and who observes brahmacarya or celibacy will attain perfection in forty days." When the kuṇḍalinī has been awakened, the yogi should practise the bhastrikā kumbhaka more and more. All the 72,000 nāḍīs are purified only when the kuṇḍalinī is awakened.

The Gheraṇḍa Saṁhitā emphasises that one should do the śakticālanaṁ first and then go on to the yoni mudrā, and that without the śakticālanaṁ the yoni mudrā is not complete.

Yoni mudrā

The yoni mudrā is described in the Gheraṇḍa Saṁhitā thus:

TECHNIQUE: Sit in the siddhasana. Close the ears with the thumbs, the eyes with the index fingers, the nostrils with the middle fingers, the upper lip with the ring fingers and the lower lip with the little fingers. Inhale and exhale through the lips, rolling the lips as if you are about to whistle (which is known as the kākī mudra or the crow-beak mudra). Contemplate the kuṇḍalinī and rouse the śaktī by repeating the mantra 'huṁ hamsaḥ' and take it to the thousand-petalled lotus in the crown of the head. (If you wish to you may relax the middle fingers a little when you wish to inhale and exhale, instead of the kakī mudra).

The Yogānuśāsanaṁ gives a different technique:

TECHNIQUE: Inhale. As you do so, direct the mind towards the base of the spine to the perineum (the yoni). Now do the mūlabandha by contracting the perineum. Visualise the prāṇa entering the radiant suṣumnā-nāḍī. Exhale. Visualise the prāṇa moving up the spine to drink the nectar at the feet of the lord in the crown of the head, descending to the base and once again rising to the crown of the head. This is yoni mudrā, which bestows all psychic powers and liberation on the yogi.

Śāmbhavi mudrā

TECHNIQUE: Concentrate internally on any of the psychic centres. Keep the eyes open, fixedly looking at an object at a distance of about two feet. Look without seeing, and without winking.

The Gheraṇḍa Saṁhitā asks that the eyes be turned towards the eyebrow centre and that one should 'behold the self'. The Pradīpikā has a similar technique. Direct the gaze towards the centre of the eyebrows, raise the eyebrows a little, and behold the inner light; you will soon reach the unmanī state or the state of utter tranquillity. The movement of both mind and prāṇa is suspended.

(Note: A specialist in eye-training advises against the unwinking gaze when the eyes are not focused on the object that is in front of them. The argument is that the eyes feel cheated when the mind is not linked to them. However, observation shows that the baby does not blink very much and this does not harm its eyes. The mind is the real seer, the eyes are but instruments; the mind sees with the eyes closed and in the same way the mind may not wish to see when the eyes are open. A word of caution may be relevant here: when you practise the śāmbhavi mudrā seriously and often, it is good also to practise the trāṭaka – or the exercise which demands focussing the vision on the object in front.)

Hearing of nāḍa

TECHNIQUE: Sit in siddhāsana. Practise the śāmbhavi mudrā first. Close your ears with the thumbs (as in the yoni mudrā). Listen intently with your right ear to the inner sounds. Focus your mind on them. If you persist in the practice the mind will soon become tranquil and the inner sounds will shut out all external sounds and distractions. The mind will enter into the great silence, which is brahman.

Many yogis emphasise the importance of nāḍā-anusandāna (hearing of the inner mystical sounds). In this connection, it may be of interest to hear the opinion of Bhagavan Ramana Maharishi:

"Meditation on nāḍa is one of the several approved methods. Nāḍa helps concentration. After it is felt the practice should not be made an end in itself. Nāḍa is not the objective; the subject should firmly be held; otherwise a blank will result. Though the subject is there even in the blank he would not be aware of the cessation of nāḍa of different kinds. In order to be aware even in that blank one must remember his own self. Nāḍā-upāsana is good; it is better if associated with vicāra. In that case the nāḍa is made of chinmāya and also tanmāya (of knowledge and of self)." (Nāḍa-upāsana is the practice of hearing the mystical sounds. Vicāra is enquiry into the self.)

Indeed, haṭha yoga does not consider the hearing of these mystical sounds the goal, but one of the methods of bringing about quiescence of the mind. In fact, the Pradīpikā declares that for those who have no self-knowledge Goraksa has given nāḍa-upāsana which even the dull student can do.

47. THE INNER PSYCHIC WORLD

What is self-knowledge? What veils it? How do I know that such a veil of impurity exists?

To answer these questions one need not be a philosopher, metaphysician or theologian. You know you exist, but you do not know what you are. You think (or you think that you think), but you do not know what thought is. You say "I am," and you do not know what 'I' is.

This self-ignorance creates a limitation, a conditioning. In oneness it creates diversity. We live in a universe – the 'single' verse, the single manifestation of the cosmic being, in which self-ignorance creates endless divisions. We live in a cosmos (kosmos means order) in which there is perfect order, but the self-ignorance creates disorder; it sees conflict where several forces and factors complement one another.

In order to appreciate all this it is helpful to be acquainted with the vision of the perfected yogi of self-knowledge. Obviously his knowledge is not your knowledge, it is not self-knowledge, it is not valid – but it enables you to know your ignorance. This is valuable.

The entire universe and beyond are filled with cosmic consciousness; all this is nothing but pure cosmic consciousness. Being consciousness it is aware of itself, and this awareness of itself creates a seeming duality. There is awareness of the truth that consciousness is not inert but that it is all-power, all-energy; there is awareness of the infinite potentiality of the manifestation of this cosmic energy. This causes a stirring or a movement in consciousness, which is comparable to a wish arising in the individual. In the individual the wish is soon translated into action; in the cosmos this stirring is realised as the universe. Consciousness, energy and matter are different states of the one. It may be that they are what are known as satva, rajas and tamas in yoga philosophy.

When consciousness becomes aware of itself and therefore of the energy, duality and therefore space is created. This is the first evolute. Consciousness becoming aware of this space feeds this movement, and motion within space is air. That is the next evolute. Movement of air creates friction and fire is evolved. Science affirms that when two gases fuse a spark of fire is produced, and at the same time there is water. Water is the next evolute. Water cools, condenses and solidifies into the earth.

The yogi sees the universe as the body of the cosmic being. It is macrocosmic. His own body is microcosmic, non-different in essence from the macro-cosmic. He busies himself with understanding this microcosm, knowing that a total knowledge of the microcosm is at once the total knowledge of the macrocosm. Self-knowledge is the knowledge of the absolute, infinite or god.

Whatever exists in the universe is in your body, too. "In his upper member man has an image of god which shines there without pause," said Meister Eckhart. Up in the head of man is the seat of consciousness – it is not the brain cells but what is in them, what works through them, of which the cells are but the abode. When that consciousness becomes aware of itself it sees itself as the object; and that is the mind.

Consciousness itself is life, energy. Consciousness and energy differ only in their polarity and not in their substance. The movement of thought within consciousness creates space, and the other cosmic elements are evolved. As in the cosmos so in the body. Consciousness has its seat in the crown of your head, the mind is centred in the space between the eyebrows, the element space in the throat, the element air in the heart region, fire in the navel region, water in the genital area and the earth-element in the anal region.

In the Bhagavad Gītā Krishna tells us: "By a small part of my being I pervade all." There is a large residue. Cosmic consciousness-energy is immeasurable. In the microcosm, too, there is a great residual energy. Residue is 'śēṣa' in sanskrit; and 'śēṣa' also refers to a snake. Hence perhaps the yogi views this residual energy as a snake. How do we know it exists? By the fact that in a crisis or danger there is a great surge of energy whose existence we were unaware of. This residue is beyond the 'me' or ego-sense, and it is the suspension of the 'me' in crisis that seems to release it. A further proof of this is the fact that in sleep we get a small dose of this residual energy and hence we wake up refreshed; and that again is when the ego-sense is suspended.

Consciousness when it is aware of the faculty of sight (i.e., when it wills to see) shines as the eyesight and the physical eyes. Similarly the other faculties and vital organs evolved. Having thus brought these faculties into being, it identifies itself with them and develops individuation. Consciousness projecting itself as life becomes blindly involved in ignorant activity and endless, helpless automation. When it is clouded by the veil of ignorance, the truth of immortality becomes fear of death and an attempt to perpetuate oneself in one's progeny.

It is not as though consciousness has become ignorance! Just as the sky is not tainted by the cloud, and the canvas is not affected by the picture of fire that appears on it, neither consciousness nor prāṇa can ever become impure. However, there is a notion of such impurity in the nāḍīs (flow of prāṇa), which veils self-knowledge. This has to be removed. Hence, the Bhagavad Gītā hints that yoga is practised in order to purify oneself, not in order to realise god or the self (this is ever real and need not be made real).

It is easy to theorise: "I am not the body nor the mind, I am the immortal self." While such affirmation has its value and therefore use, what we are looking for is an actual transcendence, not wishful thinking. One of the methods suggested for this is haṭha yoga. The uniqueness of haṭha yoga is its recognition of the physical body itself as the crystallisation of the psyche and therefore the proper vehicle of the soul. Its philosophy is appealing since it 'stoops to conquer' and does not demand that man pull himself up by his socks.

The Bhagavad Gītā describes an inverted tree with its roots above and branches below. Consciousness which is above, polarised as prāṇa, pours down to every part of the body. Still it is one:it is all consciousness. The polarised consciousness animating the millions of cells of the body is known as the subtle body. In this there are 72,000 nāḍīs,(the Yogānuśāsanam mentions 350,000) all of which come together in the kanda (approximately the perineum).

Of these nāḍīs, three are considered most important. They are the link, as it were, between consciousness in the brain-centre and the distant organs. (In the physical body the spine is such a link between the head and the limbs.) These three principal nāḍīs are known as the iḍā, the piṅgalā and the suṣumṇā.

The iḍā and piṅgalā lie on the two sides of the suṣumṇā. Some say that they cross each other between the head and the base of the spine like the caduceus. The Yogānuśāsanam says that the iḍā lies on the left side of the central channel and terminates in the left nostril; the piṅgalā lies on the right side of the channel and terminates in the right nostril. We may overlook the different theories concerning this, since the most vital nāḍī for consideration is the suṣumṇā.

The description of the suṣumṇā in the tantrik texts is

highly inspiring. In the section dealing with antaryāga (inner adoration), a tantrik text describes the suṣumṇā as having the appearance of a walking stick – from the mūlādhāra up to the crown of the head and bending down to the nostrils. It has the luminosity of lightning and a thousand suns. Yet, it is cool on account of the nectar that flows in it. The Saṭ-cakra-nirupanaṁ says that the suṣumṇā-nāḍī is like the sun, moon and fire. It extends from the kanda to the crown of the head, while the vital part of the suṣumṇā known as vajra-nāḍī extends from the root of the genitals to the crown of the head. Within even this vajra-nāḍī is the citriṇī, which is extremely brilliant and at the same time extremely subtle. This concept demands the most intense concentration and attention. Citriṇī is pure intelligence and runs all the way through, like the vajra-nāḍī. Inside even this citrinī is the brahma-nāḍī which 'shines in the minds of sages' – i.e., pure knowledge or self-knowledge.

KUṆḌALINĪ FOR CHARACTER BUILDING

The human being is a very complex personality, but he need not suffer from the complexes that are so evident in our society today. It is true that there are numerous aspects to his character which are delicately balanced and that this balance can be easily upset by very many factors, both internal and external. At the same time, his entire personality is an integrated unit saturated with the highest degree of intelligence. Hence it should be easy to sustain the balance or restore it even if it is temporarily disturbed.

Unfortunately we have devoted too much attention to imbalanced states of the mind and to abnormal behaviour and very little, if at all, to the study of the wholeness or health of the human being. Yet the right understanding of the wholeness might provide the key to the prevention of what we wish to cure. As is being increasingly realized by medicine and psychology, it is indeed the existence of this wholeness that makes even the so-called "cure" possible.

Krishna, in the *Bhagavad Gītā,* gives a succinct description of the total human personality. It occurs in the thirteenth chapter of the text. To begin with, there are the "field" and "the knower of the field". The field is the apparently diverse components that constitute the psychophysical organisms. The knower of this whole field is the intelligence "within" which is indivisibly one with the intelligence "within all" and which we commonly refer to as God. No part of the field is unknown to the knower of the field. The knower is not only the subject of an object – as in "The eyes see the foot" or "I am aware of the pain in my back" – but the knower or the indwelling intelligence aware of the functions in this psychophysical organism that the conscious mind is unaware of. That the conscious part of the mind is unaware of these functions is irrelevant; perhaps it is meant to be so, even as the nose is not meant to hear or to see. More than even this, this indwelling intelligence by its very nature is aware of itself, in a non-subject-object fashion. It is self-knowledge, knowledge which is the self or self which is knowledge. Hence Krishna declares that it is the knower of all.

In the same chapter is given the clue to creation and therefore to the operation of the creative intelligence: "It is on account of the interaction between this knower and the field that a being arises here, moving or unmoving". It is the knower, the indwelling intelligence that determines the character of every component part of the field.

The component parts of the field are thus enumerated in the same chapter of the scripture: "the cosmic elements, egosense, buddhi or the determining intellect, the unmanifest nature, the ten senses with the mind as the eleventh; the objects of the five senses, desire and hate, happiness and unhappiness, the intelligence that holds everything together and the cohesive force. One is tempted to see a distinction here between the cosmic elements and their individualized counterparts, but such distinction can at best be arbitrary and ficticious. All this is the field. The knower of the field is the very heart, the creator and the reality of this field, and that which is aware of the field at all times.

The individualized intellect (the inner intelligence) enables one to think, to reason and to observe the physical actions and the psychological states. But the cosmic creative intelligence is the overall observer of the whole field and is reflected in the medium of a small part of itself which then becomes the individualized intelligence. The individualized intellect is able to observe and perhaps detect a fault, but the remedy is found and the fault is remedied only by the creative intelligence. When the fault is remedied, wholeness or health or holiness is restored to the whole personality.

That is what yoga is about. That is what meditation means. The diagnosis is made but the intellect, the individualized intelligence, which then turns within in prayerful adoration to set the creative intelligence in motion to heal the organism and restore the inner harmony and balance.

All this is especially true of behavioural or psychological problems.

The cosmic intelligence which created diverse objects in 'the field' evolved them from the unmanifest and the five cosmic elements (space-time, air, fire, water and earth) which are also part of the field. In their subtlest forms they are unmanifest. In their less subtle forms they themselves form the perceiving senses. In their gross forms they are themselves the objects of these senses. These three forms of the element interact upon one another constantly and their equilibrium is often disturbed. On the gross sphere or plane these disturbances are known as diseases and on the psychological plane they are the character defects.

In order to help with the detection of these various disturbances of the inner harmony or disequilibrium among the elements that constitute the psychophysical being, the yogi has mapped out certain fields within the wider field described above. These fields are again represented by mandalas which are geometrical configurations, intricately worked out and woven with inspiring symsolism. Here is an outline of the whole scheme which is well worth meditating upon.

The mandalas are the six chakras or psychic centres which the yogi believes actually exist in the subtle body which corresponds in some respects to the physical body. They are: mūlādhāra, svadhiṣṭhāna, maṇipūra, anāhata, viśuddha and ājñā. The sahasrāra is usually not considered a chakra, but as the culmination of all these and the fulfilment of the six. In what is known as

Kuṇḍalinī Yoga the yogi contemplates these chakras in order to free the knower from the false notion that he is somehow separate from the field and is therefore imprisoned in it. The process of creation is reversed as it were and the indivisibility of the creative or cosmic intelligence is realised by the yogi who is made directly aware that these six centres are in fact, in truth and for ever in the sahasrāra or the seat of cosmic creative consciousness. At the same time, there exists in these chakras a potential for character building which has not been sufficiently explored.

Each of these six chakras represents one of the five elements, the sixth being the mind. Each one has a certain geometrical design at the very core of it, and the encircling field is depicted as a lotus with different number of petals. In the pericarp of this lotus dwell divine (male and female), animal and elemental forces. The deities presiding over these mandalas also symbolically wield several weapons. Certain mantras or mystic syllables are inscribed on these petals and in their pericarp. All these chakras are said to exist in the subtle sushuṁna nāḍī which is said to be the spiritual counterpart of the spinal cord.

The general scheme of the mandalas is obvious. The body, the senses and the mind are evolved out of the five elements and the individualised intelligence. The elements have their own characteristics, bestowed on them by their presiding deities. These deities are male-female configurations, suggesting that the characteristics too may be masculine and feminine. Not only that, the deities are supported by animal forms, suggesting that the characteristics have their animal aspects, too. Thus, the basic characteristic of the element is acted upon by the masculine, the feminine, and the animal propensities. They can be positive or negative or neutral.

The words 'masculine', 'feminine' and 'animal' are used in this note only in a symbolic and spiritual sense, and there is not the slightest hint of a suggestion of superiority or inferiority. These three words could easily be substituted by 'satva', 'rajas' and 'tamas' with equal validity, but without any suggestion of comparison.

We should not forget the other factors mentioned by Krishna. For, all these characteristics are also motivated by desire (likes) and hate (dislikes) which in their (re)turn operate as happy and unhappy experiences, all these (likes and dislikes, and happiness and unhappiness) are also part of the field, with an overall binding (self-ignorant!) intellect which considers itself an ego.

The ideal is to find the optimum equilibrium or balance among all these forces. Then there is health, wholeness, holiness, harmony, love and peace – elements of character we love to see in ourselves and in others. Let us not forget that evil is not the existence of one or the other factors in creation, but an imbalance among them. Malfunction of the psychophysical organism is the indication of an imbalance. The yogi trained in meditating upon these chakras or mandalas becomes directly aware of the particular field in which such imbalance has arisen and what the nature of that imbalance is. The chakras are the tuning points in our own subtle body which interact with the corresponding factors in the cosmos. By intense contemplation and prayerful adoration of the deity presiding over the particular mandala and (through that deity) of the indwelling cosmic intelligence (God), the yogi appeals to God to remedy the character defect and to restore the balance. If we realise that intense contemplation is the moulder of character and that it is such contemplation when misdirected that brought about perversion of character, we can appreciate that contemplation of the chakras should restore the balance and remedy the character deficiencies.

Let us examine the mandalas one by one and see what they stand for.

MŪLĀDHĀRA CHAKRA: It is the chakra or mandala that is at the base of the spine. The word 'mūlādhāra' means 'the root-support'. It is where the body rests on the floor. It is at the very root of the spine or the sushuṁna nāḍī. It represents the earth-element. It is that part of the back which is in contact with the earth. The yellow square is the mystic sign-language for the earth-element. The mantra is lam – phonetically similar to 'land'–for the earth. However, on the four petals that ring the mandala are found the mantras: vam, sam, sam, sam. The mantra lam rides the elephant, the animal in the mandala. It is presided over by the Brahma, the male creator, and by Dākinī as the female counterpart.

The earth-element is firm and strong enough to support the diverse beings. It represents the sense of smell and the function of locomotion (the feet which are in contact with the earth). Earth is solid. It supports all. It is the nourisher of all beings. It is also the graveyard of all. It is both the source and the end. It is hard and firm. It is always beneath everyone's feet and is trampled upon by all – it is patient and forebearing.

From all these evolves a beautiful picture of the psychological characteristics that are associated with this mandala, and we get a clue to their relation to our character and behaviour. The masculine quality of hardness and inflexibility should in a state of balance be matched by the female quality of forbearance and forgiveness. One without the other is imbalance. The earth as the nourishing mother is also the grave that swallows us all. It is possible that we pay excessive attention to "youthfulness and vigour" and too little to the inescapable fact that all this should one day come to an end. We might be tempted to boast of our origins or our beginnings and ignore the inevitable end. All these imbalances reflect in our behaviour as perversions.

On the physical level, the earth-element represents the sense of smell and the function of locomotion or the use of legs. The defective function of the earth-element in the body might lead to illnesses in these two areas. The elephant is strong but slow-moving. We need the strength of the elephant, but not its sluggishness.

Deep and devout contemplation of the details of the mandala in the muladhara will restore the balance. Such contemplation also enables us to avoid undesirable elements, to promote those qualities that we lack, and to sublimate our nature. To do all this it is not necessary to indulge in auto-suggestion or affirmations. Intense contemplation of the mandalas is sufficient.

The mandala is also ringed with tridents on all sides, suggesting that (a) the characteristics of the element spread out in all directions, covering all aspects of one's life, and (b) the wholesome effects of contemplation on the centre are protected from obstacles which may approach from any direction.

SVĀDHIṢṬHĀNA CHAKRA: This chakra is related to the genitals. The element represented is water (which is obvious) and the nectar of immortality (which is again obvious since it is related to the faculty of reproduction). The mantra is vaṁ (phonetically analogous to water). The geometrical sign is a crescent moon: presumably because the moon is somehow related to the tides. The animal is makara or the aquatic alligator which is extremely strong in water (hence, symbol of virility) and which feeds upon an unwary prey. The lotus has six petals on which are prescribed the six syllables baṁ bhaṁ maṁ, yaṁ raṁ laṁ. The presiding deities are Vishnu (male) and Rakinī (female).

We are concerned with the element water, male Vishnu and female Rakinī, and the animal alligator. The qualities of water are: life-giving and life-destroying (as in floods, drowning, etc.), raining and evaporating, thirst-producing (on account of perspiration) and thirst-quenching, taking the line of least resistance normally and also breaking down all resistance as when breaching a dam, causing obstruction (as a river across one's path) but supporting the vessel (boat) which overcomes this obstruction, the ability to finds its own level, flowing from a higher to the lower level, normally cool but capable of boiling, normally liquid but capable of hardening and also vanishing, dissolving substances, conveying taste, source of energy, cleansing. Water also symbolises life, immortality and wisdom.

Physiologically, an imbalance at this centre can manifest as disturbance in the sense of taste as also malfunctioning of the hands which arc both related to the water element. Water is variable in its quality; and the extremes (vapour and ice) are states of imbalance. Even so is heightened sensitivity of the sense of taste as undesirable as greatly weakened sensitivity.

Psychologically, the water-element is associated with several qualities which, again, can be masculine, feminine or animal. Supercilious pity, loving compassion, unhelpful sympathy; life-promoting service, gentle ministration, insincere profession of kindness (crocodile tears); giving and receiving at the appropriate time, at the inappropriate time, unpredictably; a balanced state of mind, heartless indifference, a hypocritical suppression of emotion; stimulating or satisfying positively, negatively, aimlessly; the humility of the noble, weak-willed cowardice, callous destructiveness; the psychological freedom of the spirit, unpredictability, erratic temperament; wisdom that dissolves all conflicts and contradictions, the unrestrained or untrained behaviour, speech that spreads conflicts and contradictions; vigous in all its constructive, destructive, neutral aspects; and, in general, a cool temperament and a clean heart.

We are not looking for "this" *or* "that" in all this, but for a happy balance between the positive, the negative and the neutral aspects. When this balance is disturbed and when the individualised intelligence (intellect) detects the imbalance, contemplation of the inner intelligence that manifests as the water-element at this centre will exert a correcting influence.

MAṆIPŪRA CHAKRA: It is the chakra that is related to the solar plexus or the navel. The element represented is fire (which is obvious – the *solar* plexus and the gastric *fire*). The mantra is raṁ (raṁ for red, the colour of fire?). The geometrical sign is a red triangle. The animal is the raṁ. The lotus at this centre has ten petals on which are inscribed the ten syllables from daṁ to phaṁ. The presiding deities are Rudra (male) and Lākinī (female).

The qualities of fire are: luminosity, the heat that is generated by intense activity, burning and consuming nature, generation of energy (it is interesting that this aspect is shared by fire with water which can also generate energy; and hence in this aspect it is closely related to the svādhiṣṭhāna chakra – sexual arousal may be experienced at both the centres and misdirected sexual energy may manifest as compulsive eating, bad temper and rage), constant upward movement, warmth purifying, all-destroying, creative fire of the sun, cooking and maturing food and fruits, digestion, motion, transmutation of substances and elements, the mediation between the seen and the unseen (and hence between gods and humans). Besides all this, fire paradoxically creates something (smoke) which veils it and the sun (another form of fire) gives rise to clouds which veil it. A ram is a sacrificial animal, representing self-sacrifice.

Physiologically, the element is linked to sight, the organ of excretion (anus) as part of the gastric or alimentary system and the faculty of speech, and their malfunction is indication of imbalance of the fire element.

Psychologically, the following faculties and characteristics are associated with the three (male, female and animal) aspects of fire: warmth of heart which may take the forms of violent passion, tender emotion or brutal lust; energy and dynamism which may be active or passive or dull; emotional and intellectual clarity; tendency to move up and evolve; tendency toward purity; destruction of the impure, the pure and all else; the fire of wisdom; the fire of renunciation and self-sacrifice; creative activity and destructive activity; the ability to assimilate thoughts and ideas and mature them into wisdom; austerity which transmutes undesirable qualities and characteristics into noble and exemplary spiritual qualities; fiery speech or inspiring speech. Most of these even desirable characteristics are capable of generating pride as their by-product which can then veil the very faculty that gave rise to it. Even the colour of the petals in the Maṇipūra is that of the dark rain-bearing cloud. In this respect as smoke, this aspect is related to the Anāhata which is of a smoky colour.

Patanjali in his Yoga Sutras (III.29) declares that contemplation of this chakra leads to knowledge of the body and its functions, obviously because this is the centre of the life-force.

ANĀHATA CHAKRA: It is related to the heart (and perhaps the lungs, too). The element represented is air (which again is obvious, because it is close to the lungs and to the oxygenation of the blood). The mantra is yam (phonetically similar to air). The geometrical sign is a smoky hexagon. The animal is a black antelope, swift-footed and restless. The lotus has twelve petals of crimson colour on which are inscribed the syllables from kam to tham. The presiding deities are male Isa (Śiva) and female Kākinī. Below the deity is the jīvatma or the soul, which is like the steady tapering flame of a lamp.

Air moves in all directions. It is unseen though its presence can be felt. It is powerful, though it appears to be weak and non-resisting. It is life-giving and life-sustaining, though it can at times become destructive, as in gales and cyclones. It carries scents. Like water, it flows from dense areas to light areas. It has a dual relationship with fire, which it promotes and puts out.

Physiologically, air is linked to the sense of touch and the the organ of generation, as also to the respiratory mechanism. The imbalance between the male and the female, the animal and the elemental aspects in this centre can affect these organs and senses.

Psychologically this is a very important centre if we remember that even the very soul of our being abides there. The air-element is associated with diverse qualities. The mind is unsteady and easily distracted, like the antelope and like the wind, or, the faculty of comprehensive vision exists. The emotion of love cannot be seen but is experienced at heart; this may be a mere emotion or pure devotion. (It represents also secrecy, deep devotion, sneaking suspicion or treachery). The soul-force is strong or weak; it is either irresistible or non-resisting. Love is life-giving, creative and sustaining, but as attachment is destructive all round. Love again is like a sweet fragrance which emanates and radiates from the heart. As compassion, love seeks the lowly, the needy and the afflicted. This love of the heart gets sometimes involved in passion (associated with the manipūra Chakra) and sometimes it uplifts passion to its own spiritual level.

There is a spiritually significant feature in this chakra. It is the intertwining triangles. The triangle with apex downwards represents the descent of the divine, and the triangle with apex upwards is the ascending seeker. It is here at the heart, at the seat of the soul, that all of life's energies are gathered and offered to the divine, which graciously descends to receive the gift of the self. All is not utterly clear and pure yet, and hence the colour of the chakra is smoky with red petals.

Patanjali in his Yoga Sutras (III.34) declares that contemplation of this chakra leads to a knowledge of the mind.

VISHUDDHA CHAKRA: It is related to the throat. The element represented is space (perhaps because space is related to sound and sound is related to the throat). The mantra is haṁ (the sound that you hear when you enter an empty cave and hence associated with space). The geometrical sign is the white full circle. The animal is the elephant. The lotus at this centre has sixteen petals of smoky colour with all the sixteen sanskrit vowels inscribed on them. The presiding deities are male Sadāśiva and female Sākinī. However, Sadāśiva himself is hermaphrodite. Even the male-female (positive-negative) distinction is almost overcome. Hence perhaps the Yoga Sutras of Patanjali declare that contemplation on this chakra enables the seeker to overcome hunger and thirst (III.30).

The primary qualities of space are: it is ever yielding, encompassing all, intangible and inconceivable, all sustaining without attachment to anything – hence it is often used as the symbol of the supreme Being, Brahman. It is the conveyor of sound and hence knowledge. It is immovable like the elephant.

Physiologically, this centre is related to the vocal cords and also the faculty of hearing.

Psychologically, this centre has all positive characteristics. There is a tendency to live and let others live, to yield space to all without let or hindrance. This is a great improvement upon the previous quality of love. Whereas love at the 'heart' – level can be hurt (hence the smoky colour of the petals), the purity at the throat centre cannot be hurt, and it cannot hurt either (Viśuddha means purity). It is enduring, unchanging, immeasurable and inconceivable, though it can be vague. Here the passion which was transformed into love is totally transmuted into the realisation of the indivisibility of life and oneness of love. When these noble qualities are lacking or weak, contemplation of this chakra will promote them.

ĀJÑĀ CHAKRA: It is related to the centre of the eyebrows. The mind is represented here. Oṁ is the mantra. It has no geometrical symbol at all. Nor is there an animal. The lotus here has two petals with the syllables haṁ and kṣaṁ inscribed on them. The presiding deity is the female Hākinī, with the formless Śiva.

This is beyond the manifest universe of the five elements. This chakra represents, therefore, the unmanifest nature of the substance whose appearance is the universe. There are no animal tendencies here. The text declares that it is here that the seeker has a vision of God, like a flash of lightning.

SAHASRĀRA: Sahasrāra is not a chakra, properly speaking. But it is of interest to note that in the very centre of the sahasrāra, as it were, the seeker is encouraged to contemplate the lotus-like feet of his own guru. Patanjali declares that one who contemplates this centre attains a vision of the sages and saviours of the universe, their blessings and their guidance. (III.32)

All these characteristics and faculties are beyond the reach of the mind or of the physical being, but are accessible to the intelligence within where the individual meets the cosmic, where the soul meets god. It is when that intelligence is clouded or stupified that an imbalance in them arises. Hence, it is only when that intelligence is awakened and directed to the centres involved in the imbalance that the fault can be rectified. The awakening of this intelligence is the function of Kuṇḍalinī Yoga. Kuṇḍalinī is the power, part of which is distributed throughout the body for its sustenance and day-to-day functioning, but which is otherwise dormant. Its awakening is achieved by various methods which may be learnt from a guru, and by the grace of guru or god.

While that is the indisputable way of directing the awakened intelligence to the various cakras, I venture to suggest that even intense and prayerful visualisation of the cakras by anyone may exert a wholesome influence on the centres and bring about the desired change in one's personality and character. This will happen when the intelligence is awakened and turns to the divine (the cosmic creative intelligence) in prayerful adoration.

The snag however is that in a state of inner imbalance such intense contemplation may be all but impossible. Such contemplation is possible only when the mind is utterly calm. Hence, again, if the student is guided by a competent and intelligent guru, the student can be trained to appreciate the hidden potentialities for character building that this branch of yoga holds.

The Gheraṇḍa Saṁhitā provides a brief description of the five elemental cakras. Concentration (dhāraṇā) on them is advised. The Saṁhitā, however, simplifies the theme, selecting only the vital essentials in each cakra – the geometrical sign, the word-symbol and the presiding deity. Intense concentration on each for a period of two and a half hours bestows on the yogi mastery over that element. The Saṁhitā recommends that the earth-cakra (mūlādhāra) and the water-cakra (svādhiṣṭhāna) should be placed in the heart for this purpose. Some yogis, who feel that by concentrating on the lower centres one runs the risk of rousing baser instincts, visualise them in the heart.

Some serious students of yoga have sought to combine contemplation of the cakras with the practice of the yoga āsanas. For instance: mūlādhāra for uḍḍīyāna bandha while seated, svādhiṣṭhāna for dhanurāsana, maṇipūra for halāsana, anāhata for gomukhāsana, viśuddha for sarvāṅgāsana, ājñā for trikoṇāsana, sahasrāra for śirasāsana. It is possible to find other yoga āsanas for these centres.

It is also possible to integrate hatha yoga with the other branches of yoga – in fact some people feel that karma yoga is haṭha yoga, since karma means action and haṭha yoga is active. All yoga practice starts with mūlādhāra. Bhakti or god-love begins at the anāhata where the jīva (individual soul) meets Śiva (the lord) and hence the intertwined ascending and descending triangles. Viśuddha is the purifier of the individual; to a devotee this is the consuming and purifying longing for god. Ājñā is the centre of illumination for the yogi, the eye of wisdom for the student of jñāna yoga, and the centre where the devotee sees god.

48. LAYA YOGA

Almost all the great masters have said that self-knowledge, god-realisation, enlightenment or liberation is possible only when the kuṇḍalinī is awakened and it reaches the sahasrāra. They have also said that this may happen after yoga practice, by the practice of meditation or devotion, or by the sheer grace of god or guru.

Even they who insist that it happens by grace alone emphasise the need for the student to engage himself in meditation and also in some yoga practices.

The method that the hatha yogi uses is known as laya yoga. Laya means merging or absorption. It is pointed out that the risk in this method is the stimulation of the lower impluses. On the other hand, with sincere and intelligent application of this technique, you can overcome and sublimate those very impulses. Yoga is not for the weak-minded but only for one who dares. If the following 'preliminary purificatory exercise' is practised diligently and sincerely, all the physical, emotional and psychic disturbances can be removed. Above all, if we have faith in god and guru their grace will remove all obstacles from our path.

Liberation is liberation from self-ignorance. Enlightenment is the realisation of self-knowledge. It is self-ignorance that conjures up division where only polarisation exists. Whereas prāṇa and apāna are complementary, self-ignorance creates a division. This division is the ego-principle. Haṭha, by bringing together the ha (positive, solar, prāṇa) and ṭha (negative, lunar, apāṇa) unites them – or recognises their indivisibility.

This first union of the prāṇa and tha apāṇa is effected in the solar plexus. When their division is thus cancelled, the ego-sense is suspended and kuṇḍalinī is awakened. The energies that flowed outward begin to flow towards their source, which is consciousness. This is laya.

In all this the yogi needs to exercise strict control of his physical being in its most vital aspects, so that there may be unified action and not haphazard movement of prāṇa. Such a control is acquired by the practise of the yoga postures and the prāṇāyāma. Dissipated energy must be gathered, for dissipated energy is a distraction and a perpetuation of self-ignorance. To do this efficiently all the energy-channels should be cleared and purified. Only when the prāṇa flows freely in all the nāḍīs can it change its course or direction. It is like the gears of a motor car. Only when the power is connected to the wheels can the latter be controlled, moved forward or stopped.

Usually, the prāṇa flows haphazardly in man without proper control or direction, as a motor car careering downhill in neutral gear. If everything seems to go right, it is only because the free ride has not yet been challenged by a turn, bump or obstruction. The yogi cannot afford to leave this vital process to chance.

The fusion of the prāṇa and the apāna at the solar plexus sparks off great power. The yogi does not let the control even over this psychic heat or energy get out of hand. Using definite techniques, he directs it to the base of the spinal cord, or more properly suṣumṇā-nāḍī, and up along this from centre to centre, from mūlādhāra to svādhiṣṭhāna to maṇipūra to anāhata to viśuddha and to ājñā. Ascent beyond to the seat of consciousness, or the thousand-petalled lotus, is effected by divine grace. After enjoying communion with the divine here, the power is brought down again through the successive cakras to enable the yogi to live and function in a divine way.

Daily the yogi visualises the whole process actually taking place. Nothing may happen for a long time – not till his heart is purified, his mind steadied and the power actually awakened. Yet the very visualisation helps him, for the concentrated mind directs the prana to those centres, corrects any defects there may be in the flow of the prana, promotes health and brings near the day on which the visualisation might be actualised.

Does the awakened kundalini purify the heart and steady the mind, or does it awaken only after the heart is purified and the mind steadied? Paramahamsa Baba Muktananda declared in one of his inspiring talks in California that it is the awakened kuṇḍalinī that leads to the vision of truth, and 'all the knots of the heart are cut asunder, all doubts dispelled and all the karmas come to an end when the supreme truth has been seen'; and he reminded his audience that the rising sun dispels darkness – it is not as though when the darkness goes the sun rises! According to Baba, the kuṇḍalinī is awakened through śakṭi-pata or the grace of the guru, who directly transmits his energy to the disciple. The guru is one who can bring about such awakening through śakṭi-pata. This statement is supported by a beautiful verse which occurs towards the conclusion of the Yoga Vāsiṣṭha. The sage Viśvāmitra says: "O Vāsiṣṭha, you have demonstrated that you are the guru by śakṭi-pata. Only he who is able to awaken god-consciousness in the disciple by a look, touch, verbal instruction or non-verbal grace, is a guru."

One thing is beyond controversy, and that is that total purification of the heart and steadiness of the mind are simultaneous with the awakening of the kuṇḍalinī and its ascent to the sahasrāra. The following exercises are aimed at this. The most vital part of the practice described below is self-purification. It is perhaps self-hypnosis; but the effect is more real and long lasting than self-hypnosis. We may not in one sitting burn all evil in us for ever, but every attempt is bound to leave a positive mark on our personality; if it does not, then you can be sure that there is a lack of sincerity or intensity of faith.

As students of self-hypnosis know, the conscious mind must be lulled in order that self-hypnotic suggestions might strike root. This is achieved by prāṇāyāma which accompanies the purificatory process. Each suggestion is then propelled by a mantra, the seed-mantra.

Understood rightly, the technique is entirely scientific, though it leans a bit heavily on psychology.

It is better before undertaking the practice of the following exercise, to thoroughly familiarise yourself with the alternate nostril breathing (prāṇāyāma), bhastrikā prāṇāyāma, sītali, khēcarī mudrā, mūlabhanda and jalāndhara bandha and yoni mudrā, described earlier in this chapter. Then the integrated practice of laya yoga described in the following pages becomes easy.

(a) Purificatory Prāṇāyāma
Nāḍī-śuddhi

This is also known as bhūta-śuddhi (purification of the elements which constitute the body). It is intended to purify the subtle body and to tune it with the divine, in order to commune with god. It is the yogi's conviction that man should become divine in order to co-mingle with the divine consciousness. In the Yoga Vāsiṣṭha (Upaśama Prakaraṇaṁ chapter 31) Prahlāda declares that one who is not Vishnu cannot worship Vishnu. And, chapter 54 of the same text gives a description similar to the following exercise, but using only the mantra Oṁ.

The first part is drying up of the sinful or impure aspect of our own personality; the second part is burning it; and the third part is wholesale rejuvenation or re-creation of a divine body with which to practise yoga.

(i)(a) Be seated in a comfortable posture. Breathe steadily. With closed eyes, visualise that the soul located in the heart is withdrawn to the top of the head; also, that all the evil tendencies in the heart have assumed the form of a dark cloud hiding in the left side of the abdomen. You may commence the simple alternate nostril prāṇāyāma even at this stage. Inhale through the right nostril, at the same time visualising the soul in the form of a flame ascending to the crown of the head. Repeat 'oṁ' mentally. While you retain the breath, visualise the dark cloud. Exhale through the left nostril. (The recommended ratio of repetitions of the mantra is 16:64:32 in every case throughout this exercise.)

(b) Breathe in through the left nostril. Mentally repeat the syllable 'yaṁ' (mantra for air). Hold the breath. Feel that the dark cloud of sin is dried up by the wind generated by the mantra. Breathe out through the right nostril, repeating the same mantra.

(Some students might wish to prolong the prāṇāyāma. For instance, in stage i.(b) it is possible to inhale through the left nostril and commence repeating the mantra 'yaṁ', hold the breath for a few seconds and exhale; and then breathe normally for a couple of minutes visualising the drying up of the cloud of sin, till this is actually experienced. Even so with the other steps in this exercise. Your own inner ruler is the best teacher and guide.)

(ii) Breathe in through the right nostril repeating the syllable 'raṁ' which is the word-symbol for fire. Hold the breath. Feel that the fire generated by the mantra burns up the dark cloud. Breathe out through the left nostril, repeating the mantra.

(iii)(a) Breathe in again through the left nostril. Meditate on the moon as being seated at the left nostril. Repeat the mantra 'ṭhaṁ'. (Thaṁ rhymes with 'rum'. The 'ṭh' is a hard t, harder than in 'tell' and not the soft sound in 'the'). Hold the breath, repeat the mantra. Visualise that the moonrays full of cool nectar are filling you with new life-force to create a new body, and cooling the fire generated by the previous 'raṁ' breathing. Breathe out through the right nostril, still repeating the mantra.

(b) Breathe in through the right again, repeating the mantra 'vaṁ' and feel that this mantra symbolising water provides the fluid for this new divine body. Hold the breath and breathe out through the left nostril repeating the same mantra. (Generally, haṭha yogis use (a) and tantriks use (b). A few masters use both. You are free to use one or the other. If you use only one, obviously the breathing pattern of (c) will change. The spirit of both (a) and (b) is exactly the same: the old sinful body has been reduced to ashes which are now sprinkled with divine nectar (which both the mantras 'ṭhaṁ' and 'vaṁ' represent) so that a new divine body may rise from it. Again, some tantriks omit the visualisation of the specifically located evil force on the left side. Once the soul is withdrawn to the head the entire body may be subjected to the purification process; but the visualisation of the specifically located evil force may make this purification more intense.)

(c) Breathe in through the left nostril, repeating the mantra 'laṁ', the mantra for earth, and feel that its power confers solidity upon the new divine body. Hold and breathe out. Drop the hands on to the lap.

(d) Breathing gently through both the nostrils, repeat the holy mantra sohaṁ – 'so' with the inhalation and 'haṁ' (pronounced as the English 'hum') with the exhalation, and visualise the soul descending into the heart from the top of the head, to occupy this new divine body – pure and holy. This can be continued for a few minutes.

The Yoga Vāsiṣṭha (Nirvāna Prakaraṇaṁ) suggests the use of the above procedure as a health-measure. It says, "When the mind is in a disturbed state, the body is weakened. Then there is blind movement of the energies which flow along wrong channels

. . . . All nourishment consumed in this state turns into poison and disease . . . . Such diseases are got rid of by the use of mantras like ya, ra, la, va, by right action, and by the service of holy men."

(b) Agnisara (Fanning the Fire)

Remain seated with your hands on your knees. Draw the abdomen in quickly and immediately relax. It is just fanlike movement of the abdomen – back and forth. You can do this well only if you are completely relaxed, though with a little persistent effort this exercise itself will help you relax. There is no hard and fast rule regarding breathing: you may go on breathing normally or you can exhale and hold. Gradually increase the number of back and forth movements, till you reach one hundred.

(c) Bhastrikā (The Bellows)

Bhastrika is a powerful prāṇāyāma or breathing exercise. All the great masters of yoga are very fond of it. Descriptions of it are always inadequate. The method can be properly understood only by watching an expert.

In this we use the abdominal muscles as a blacksmith uses his bellows. Quick and powerful movements are involved in this. When the abdomen is pulled in, the breath is powerfully expelled from the lungs through the nose, in one instalment. Be sure that you do not merely breathe out, but throw the breath out as you do while sneezing. Immediately and quickly the abdominal muscles are relaxed and the breath rushes into the lungs. About ten such expulsions should be sufficient to start with. (Gradually increase the number to twenty.) Then breathe out completely. Follow this by an almost complete inhalation. Use the chin-lock to hold the breath: hold it as long as you can. Do this thrice. You will be amazed to see your lung capacity and the retention time grow.

(i) During the first kumbhaka concentrate on the solar plexus and feel that the prāṇa is being built up there. Hold the breath as long as you can. When you feel that the energy wants to escape through the lower apertures of the body, gently contract them and stop the energy-escape. In due course you will actually experience the prāṇa vibrating both in the solar plexus and the muladhara. Before you breathe out release the chin-lock. (Sometimes the throat becomes dry during some of these breathing exercises. Either 'suck' a little butter or sip a little water. There is a tendency on the part of some to draw the abdomen in while breathing in and pushing it out during the exhalation. This must be carefully avoided.)

Take a few normal breaths.

(ii) When you retain the breath in bhastrikā the second time, mentally repeat the mantra 'haṁsah' and feel that the prāṇa from the solar plexus flows to the mūlādhāra.

(iii) On the third attempt you can feel that the power generated at the solar plexus 'strikes' the kuṇḍalinī śakti in the mūlādhāra. Mentally repeat the mantra 'huṁ' as the prāṇa strikes at the mūlādhāra.

If the bhastrikā has been practised effectively, and properly, then an actual pulsation is experienced in the mūlādhāra. The mantra 'huṁ' is repeated with each pulsation. Huṁ is the kavacabīja, the psychic protective shield. It will protect you from obstacles. It is, as it were, a ray of Śiva himself coming down to awaken the śakti in the mūlādhāra.

During the following exercises, too, whenever you feel that you are becoming dull and lethargic you can use the bhastrikā to 'build up' power.

(d) Sītalī (The Cooler)

Bhastrikā heats up the whole system. When this is followed by sītalī the excess of heat is taken away and only the power is left. It is optional.

Open your mouth. Protrude the tongue just a little, rolling it into a kind of a tube. Close the lips around this tube and breathe in through it. A cool current passes into you through this tongue-tube and cools your body. Hold the breath for a few seconds and then breathe out through the nose.

This can be done after each bhastrikā or you may not do it at all.

(e) Prāṇāyāma

Sit in padmāsana or siddhāsana. Use your right thumb to close the right nostril and the right ring and little fingers to close the left nostril. First breathe out through either both the nostrils or the right nostril alone.

Breathe in through the left. Hold. Breathe out through the right. Breathe in through the right. Hold. Breathe out through the left. This is one round. Mentally repeat your mantra. After some practice try to establish the ratio 1:4:2. Do this for about 5 or 10 rounds. Concentrate on the mūlādhāra cakra.

Continue the above. Practise mūlabandha (rectal uplift) with the prāṇāyāma, as follows. With the inhalation contract the rectum and the perineum and pull them up, feeling that the energy in this region is flowing upwards. While retaining the breath, use the same technique and pull the energy up. (If you are able to hold the breath for a long period and you are unable to hold the mūlabandha for that period, you can contract and relax several times during the retention of breath.) During exhalation relax the mūlabandha.

This prāṇāyāma when practised with the mūlabandha answers the description given in the Bhagavad Gītā: "There are others who offer prāṇa into apāna and apāna into prāṇa". There is a feeling of the prāṇa being poured into the apāna during the inhalation and apāna being poured into prāṇa during exhalation after the mūlabandha. The Yoga Vāsiṣṭha also declares: "There is no rebirth for one who offers prāṇa into apāna and apāna into prāṇa."

This is a very important exercise for awakening the kuṇḍalinī śakti. It will also enable you to sublimate the sex-energy.

You can do this prāṇāyāma about 10 times in all.

Throughout the exercise keep repeating your mantra.

(f) Khecarī mudra

Visualise a psychic tube running along the centre of the spine connecting the centre of the eyebrows with the mūlādhāra cakra. Open your mouth just a little to let the tongue roll back and close the posterior nasal openings. Even an unsuccessful attempt to do so will ensure an internal widening of the throat. Breathe in through the open mouth. Feel a cool current pass down the tube to the mūlādhāra cakra. As you breathe in, you will make the sound 'Ah' with the lower part of the expanded throat. Hold the breath for a few seconds, concentrating on the mūlādhāra. Breathe out, feeling that hot air rises from the mūlādhāra and goes right up the tube and comes out through the top part of the expanded throat, with the sound 'Ee'. The tongue may be allowed to resume the normal position during exhalation. Practise this a few times to start with and gradually increase the number. Mentally repeat 'sohaṁ' for the downward movement of the energy and 'haṁsaḥ' for the upward movement.

While you inhale you feel the air flowing in; it is also possible to sense a feeling of 'fullness' rising within at the same time. When you exhale, there is the sense of emptying which seems to descend inwards, though the air rises up to be exhaled.

Hence, there are some yogis who visualise the current flowing up during inhalation and down for the exhalation. While there is no objection to this, the other way round seems to help tremendously in the sublimation of all energies, as there is definitely a very real feeling that the student is keen on taking all energies upwards – it is as if the lord stretches his hand from the sahasrāra and pulls all the energies in the cakras up to himself. The Yoga Vāsiṣṭha describes the mystic process by which kuṇḍalinī is aroused by inhalation and made to rise up; the kuṇḍalinī thereupon absorbs all the other nāḍīs and rises through the suṣuṁnā as the yogi exhales.

In khēcarī mudrā the polarity (of consciousness above and energy below) is actually visualised; and in the next, yoni mudrā, the absorption is effected.

(g) *Yoni mudrā*

Yoni is womb. The word mudrā has several meanings, one of which is 'that which makes happiness flow'. Just as the unborn child is enclosed within the womb, even so by this mudrā we enclose our consciousness entirely within the self, without allowing it to be externalised. By the practice of this mudrā the fountain-source of happiness is tapped – hence, it is called mudrā.

This mudrā is best practised in the siḍḍhāsana. In siḍḍhāsana the two lower openings in the body are closed. Now we proceed to close the others:

Block the ears with the thumbs, close the eyes with the index fingers, the nose with the middle fingers, the upper lips with the ring fingers and the lower ones by the little fingers. Lift the middle fingers a little when you want to breathe in and out.

Breathing: Inhale. During the inhalation and during the period of the retention of breath, fix the attention on the cakra concerned. During the exhalation contract inwardly (and if possible outwardly) the region of that cakra, so that you have a firm hold on it. Draw the abdomen in during exhalation. When the exhalation is complete, hold the lungs empty for a few seconds and during this period feel that the energy is moving to the next cakra. Thus you may have one retention of breath at each cakra.

(i) Concentrate on the mūlādhāra cakra. Mentally repeat the mantra 'oṁ laṁ'. Meditate on the yellow square (the symbol of earth-element). Practise mūlabandha (rectal uplift). Feel the kuṇḍalinī śakti is moving upwards to the next centre. As it travels up, repeat the mantra 'haṁsaḥ' mentally.

(Since the 'observer of the cakras' still seems to be at the eyebrow centre, the colour visualised naturally pervades the whole body with the point of radiation in the respective centre. It is also rational because every element is everywhere in the whole body.)

(ii) Next, concentrate on the svādhiṣṭhāna cakra at the tip of the spine in the region of the genitals. Repeat the mantra 'oṁ vaṁ'. Meditate on the 'crescent moon' (the symbol of water-element). Practise mūlabandha again. Feel the kuṇḍalinī śakti is moving upwards to the next centre. As it travels up, repeat the mantra 'haṁsaḥ'. In the same way, take the śakti to:

(iii) Manipūra cakra (behind the navel region) – mantra 'oṁ raṁ' – red triangle (symbol of fire-element).

(iv) Anahāta cakra (behind the heart region) – mantra 'oṁ yaṁ' – smoky hexagon of two interlaced triangles (symbol of air-element).

(v) Viśuddha cakra (throat, behind the Adam's apple) – mantra 'oṁ haṁ' – white circle (the symbol of ether-element).

(vi) Ājnā cakra (between the eyebrows) – mantra 'oṁ'.

(vii) From here visualise the śakti ascending up to the sahasrāra at the crown of the head and enjoying blissful union with the lord. No special mantra has been mentioned for the sahasrāra. In fact, it is not regarded as a cakra at all, it being the psychic abode of all the energies dwelling ordinarily in all the six lower centres. It is usual to meditate upon the lotus feet of the guru or the supreme lord in that centre (if it is regarded as such). The Gheraṇḍa Saṁhitā asks the yogi to meditate in the pericarp of the sahasrāra, visualising there a lotus of twelve petals, white in colour, and with the twelve mantras ha, sa, kṣa, ma, la, va, ra, yuṁ, ha, sa, kha, phreṁ. Within this there is a triangle with the mantras a, ka, tha on the sides and ha, la, kṣa at the angles. The mantra for this centre is oṁ. On it there is the jewelled seat where the feet or the sandals of the guru rest. (If all this sounds a bit complicated, the following may be helpful: when with the yoni mudrā the śakti has been taken up to ājñā, drop the hands on the lap and meditate. During this meditation visualise the consciousness linking the ājñā with the lotus feet of the guru in the sahasrāra. When this is achieved, then with the further inhalation and exhalation it is easy to feel the energy flowing up and down this channel: i.e.

the prayer flowing up and the grace of the guru flowing into the ājñā.)

Baba Muktananda Paramahaṃsa (who is one of the greatest living yogis and who gives śakti-pāta) asks all yoga students to meditate with 'so-haṁ' – 'so' during inhalation and 'haṁ' during exhalation – feeling that 'so' or he is the guru and 'haṁ' or I is the disciple. If you listen intently to your breath, you will actually hear the breath sing this mantra. If you look deep within, you will actually see the identity of your innermost self with your guru – identity of the aṭmā with the paramāṭmā.

All this is already elaborate. Each centre is a psychic maṇḍala or pattern. This meditation is an elaborate practice leading the mind from the gross to the subtle, from the physical to the psychic and to the spiritual. Laya yoga involves meditating upon each cakra, in all its details as set out in the last chapter. Meditate on the deity there, and with his blessings gather up the mantras on the petals of the cakra and merge them into the bīja or the seed-mantra. Then raise the bija or the seed-mantra on to the next one, where it spreads out into the next mandala. If all this is done with intense concentration, faith, devotion and keenness the effect is indescribable.

When you wish to terminate your meditation, get back to the yoni mudra position and continue the cakra meditation in the reverse order. The technique is the same as for the ascent of the kuṇḍalinī, except that as the śakti moves from one cakra to the one lower down, the mantra used is 'sohaṁ'.

During the meditation on the ājñā cakra feel that the kuṇḍalinī derives immense power, peace and bliss from the union with the lord. As the śakti descends into the various cakras, feel that this power is being distributed at those centres. (Incidentally, this meditation can vivify the entire nervous system and the body.)

While watching the breath during meditation the following technique can be adopted. Besides the psychic benefit, it has the unique advantage of maintaining the attention on the suṣuṁnā (the mystic or psychic channel within the spine) which we endeavoured to cultivate by the previous exercises.

Remember the walking-stick shaped psychic tube? Visualise that it bends down to the navel region (the solar plexus) or the heart on the right side of the chest. Thus the 'stick' has the shape of the letter C, more or less. As you inhale, feel the psychic current coursing down the C-tube from the centre of the eyebrows down to the solar plexus (or the heart); when you exhale, feel that this direction is reversed, starting from the solar plexus (or the heart), going down to the base of the spine, up the spine and forward to the centre of the eyebrows.

This technique can be adopted whenever you feel like concentrating on the breath – even during the prāṇāyāma exercises, during the laya yoga or otherwise.

Healing: Always pray and radiate healing rays to all those in need, before rising from the meditation seat. This is a great service to humanity.

Conclusion

The effectiveness of laya yoga lies in powerful imagination (which is image-in-action: i.e. transferring the image of god within, visualising god within and feeling his living presence there). The emotional risks involved can surely be avoided if the 'purificatory breathing exercise' is practised with intense visualisation and feeling. This blossoms into experience. That is what the sculptor does. He looks at the stone and visualises the statue he wants to carve out of it. He sees it there. He persists in this visualisation till the chips that do not belong to the statue are chiselled away. Now his imagination or visualisation has become actualised, realised. The 'purificatory breathing exercise' itself can be used to overcome any evil habit – physical or mental. Instead of vaguely imagining that all the evil tendencies are stored in the left side of the abdomen, you can actually visualise the particular evil habit there; and then visualise that habit being dried and burnt. That is the obvious purpose of prefacing the laya yoga practice with the important and vital process of purification.

To reject the practice of laya yoga fearing the risk of undesirable physical or mental results, is like throwing out the baby with the bath-water. Yoga is for the brave man full of commonsense and wisdom, with discrimination to absorb what is good and guard himself against what is undesirable. The caution found in the texts on yoga applies only to those who devote their whole time to the practice of yoga; and even then only if they refuse to heed nature's warnings in the form of pain, discomfort, etc. Fear not.

Regular practise of yoga will dispel all your doubts and bestow the highest prize upon you.

The sage Vāsiṣṭha says: "By any one of these methods propounded by the various teachers, the movement of prāṇa can be restrained. These yogic methods bring about the desired results if they are practised without violence or force. When one is firmly established in such practice with simultaneous growth in dispassion, and when the mental conditioning comes under perfect restraint, there is fruition of the restraint of the movement of prāṇa. Surely, all these practices appear to be distractions; but by their steady practise, one reaches the absence of distractions. It is only by such steady practice that one is freed from sorrow and he experiences the bliss of the self. Hence, practise yoga. When through practice the movement of prāṇa is restrained, then nirvāna or liberation alone remains." (Upaśama Prakaraṇaṁ of Yoga Vāsiṣṭha: 79.)

However, all these when practised mechanically are of no use at all. Hence the same Vāsiṣṭha declares that the energies in the body are purified only through jñāna or spiritual insight. That is the teaching of Bhagavān Ramana Maharishi, too. He says, "Breath control is said to help the yogi to rouse the kuṇḍalinī–śakti which lies coiled in the solar plexus. The śakti rises through the nāḍī called the suṣumnā, which is embedded in the core of the spinal cord and extends to the brain . . . . If one concentrates on the sahasrāra, there is no doubt that the ecstasy of samāḍhi ensues. The vāsanās (tendencies) are, however, not destroyed."

The Haṭha Yoga Pradīpikā therefore defines laya as 'The non-recollection of past experiences'. Till all the vāsanās or memories of past experiences are destroyed, one should practise laya.

SUGGESTED SEQUENCE FOR THE PRACTICE OF HAṬHA YOGA

Āsanas

1. Sūryanamaskāra – at least twelve rounds

2. Śirasāsana	3. Sarvāṅgāsana
4. Halāsana	5. Matsyāsana
6. Paścimottānāsana	7. Bhujangāsana
8. Śalabhāsana	9. Dhanurāsana
10. Ardhamatsyendrāsana	11. Mayūrāsana
12. Pādahastāsana	13. Cakrāsana
14. Trikoṇāsana	15. Śavāsana

Prāṇāyāma

1. The purificatory prāṇāyāma given in Laya Yoga (a).
2. Bhastrikā – three rounds, with mūlabandha during the kumbhaka.
3. Sītalī – three rounds.
4. Alternate nostril breathing (i) without kumbhaka, (ii) with kumbahaka after inhalation and (iii) with kumbhaka after exhalation also – ten rounds each.
5. Bandha-trāya (the triple lock – mūlabandha with inhalation, jālandhara bandha also with the retention, uḍḍīyāna bandha also with the exhalation, and then hold all three together for a few moments).
6. Yoni mudrā – for a minimum of three kumbhakas.
7. Bhrāmarī (and then meditation).

Chapter Five

RĀJA YOGA

49. Yoga of Meditation

"The glass may be made of gold, but what makes the glass useful is the place where there is no gold – the empty space." (Taoist maxim.) That is meditation. It is not the feverish activity in which you are engaged constantly that ensures your prosperity, but the period when you are in meditation. That is the creative vacuum, that is the creative silence, the creative peace.

Hence, yogi Svātmārāma declares in the Haṭha Yoga Pradīpikā: "Without haṭha, rāja yoga is not fruitful: and haṭha is not fruitful, is not fulfilled without rāja yoga. Hence one must practise both. At the conclusion of the kumbhaka and the restraint of prāṇa, one should make the mind supportless (unconditioned). Then one will attain the goal of rāja yoga."

All this is laconically expressed in the Yoga Sūtras of Patanjali. He declares that the mental modifications cease when the breath is suspended after being expelled. Then surely the mind stands supportless. That is meditation.

Gheraṇḍa however gives the student some support! Gheraṇḍa Saṁhitā describes three kinds of meditation – the gross, the luminous and the subtle:

The gross meditation involves elaborate visualisation in the region of one's heart of a heavenly abode of god who reigns supreme in that heaven. It is contemplation of god with name and form, to be visualised in elaborate detail. This is extremely popular, especially with devotees of god. The legends known as purāṇas provide the devotee with very many variations of the theme for his contemplation.

The second type is the contemplation of light. The focal point can either be the mūlādhāra cakra or the centre of the eyebrows. The student contemplates mūlādhāra cakra in all its glowing details, and visualises the light of the jīva or the living soul in the form of a radiant flame. Or, he can contemplate the light of 'oṁ' in the eyebrow centre.

The third type is regarded as 'difficult to be attained even by the gods, as it is a great mystery' in the words of the Gheraṇḍa Saṁhitā. The student practises the śāmbhavī mudra during his meditation. The kuṇḍalinī is awakened. Along with the self this kuṇḍalinī śakti (or the life-force) leaves the body through the eyes and appears in front of the yogi. This is not easy even to imagine!

Meditation is the art of realising the universal self, beyond the ego-sense. Universal is one and not many: what is it that appears to have created a division in the one so that this one appears to be many? Meditation is the quest for the answer to this question.

In the practice of the yoga āsanas we sense an intelligence which is beyond the 'me'; during the practice of prāṇāyāma, again we realise that life is governed by an intelligence that is distinct from the ego-sense. In meditation we actually pursue this ego-sense to see what it is and how it veils that intelligence. In samāḍhi or vicāra (enquiry) we discover that the ego-sense is a non-entity – it has always been a non-entity. The transcendental intelligence alone is the reality at all times. Even ignorance and enlightenment, covering and discovery, are words invented by the mind to rationalise all this.

The one is one, it only appears to be many. Even the three factors that we discussed in the last chapter (consciousness, energy and matter) are really not three but one unity apprehended at three stages. If you have watched trees in early spring (especially in countries like Canada, where the growing season is brief) you see this clearly. In winter the trees have no foliage at all. Early in spring you go near a tree and watch: the tree knows the season, the temperature and the climatic conditions; it has also the knowhow of sprouting fresh leaves. When these sprouts emerge triumphantly, you see the action of the energy, the will, and then you see its materialisation.

Such division of this phenomenon into knowledge, will and action (or consciousness, energy and matter) is not a fact but the fruit of your own mental conditioning. You think that one has become three and then you think that the three are somehow one. As long as this thinking thinks that it thinks, it will continue to think diversely – creating contradictions, conflicts and conditioning; happiness and unhappiness; fear and anxiety.

You think that you are unhappy and therefore you feel unhappiness. It is true that there is a temporary benefit if you come face to face with the truth that you are unhappy only because you think you are unhappy. You know that this unhappiness is not something real in itself, but is the product of your thinking. All the great movements which pretend to cure all ills by enabling one to think one way or the other are based on this wonderful formula. But unless this discovery is your own, you do not know how to think! You think you are unhappy, so you feel unhappy. The obvious inference here is that if you think you are happy, you will feel happy! Theoretically it seems to be sensible, but only theoretically. It does not work because you do not know what it is that thinks. In the case of the unhappiness which you are experiencing now, the thinking is there already. You are not producing anything, it is there and you are observing it; whereas in the other case, are you thinking that you are happy, or are you thinking that you are thinking that you are happy? The happiness is twice removed! You are only sitting and thinking that you are thinking that you are happy. In other words, do you know what this thinking means? Who thinks? That is the problem.

There is another problem. You are seriously observing a thought (let us say of anger) and you think you discover that a thought of anger is later felt as anger. This apparent discovery sometimes makes it appear that the anger has gone, or it seems to have gone. Perhaps it has merely been overlaid with dullness; perhaps you are looking away inwardly because to observe the anger is painful; or perhaps, having understood all this theoretically, you imagine that in the light of your observation it has gone. A few days later it comes back! That means it was there, hidden all the time, covered with a lot of thinking and imagination. When it is thus covered, there is no longer the pain to provide the incentive to look within. What do you do now? You look within. Everything is calm (or appears so). The mind has not been conquered. A few days later somebody else provokes you and suddenly you realise that anger was there all the time – but you were 'asleep'. So during that period of dullness you lose the edge, the incentive. What must you do?

The yogi suggests that you practise an exercise. As you inhale, repeat the mantra mentally. As you exhale, repeat the mantra mentally. As this mental repetition of the mantra goes on, the mind forms a habit. This habit is not looked upon by the mind as a threat or a challenge. (If breathing itself is not a challenge to the mind, then this automatic repetition of the mantra is not a challenge either.) The mind is not bothered at all. The habit is formed.

You sit listening to your own mental repetition of the mantra. You hear the mantra. Who is it that is repeating the mantra? 'Me.' Who is it that is listening to the mantra? 'Me.' Now there is a new incentive to watch the mind. The thing that repeats the mantra inside and the thing that listens to the mantra inside both seem to be your objects of observation – and you are watching both these. You can similarly observe anger or other psychological factors now

Only a calm mind can observe itself, can reflect. Any reflection that takes place in a distracted mind is a perversion. You can neither meditate nor reflect when the mind is in commotion. Whatever is reflected when the reflecting medium is disturbed is a distortion. You cannot make the mind calm, because any effort to do so is going to disturb the calmness of the mind, is going to alter the essential nature of the mind. All the methods that people have invented (including the methods of visualising an image of god) are confessions of failure, though they are excellent aids. You do not know how to still the mind; and therefore, instead of allowing the mind to think of a million things, you make it think of just one thing – call it Krishna, Buddha, Jesus, Moses or a mantra. When you successfully plant this mantra or image of god in the mind, you have only succeeded in creating one huge tidal wave in the mind – with the result that all the little waves disappear.

Hence Krishna in the Bhagavad Gītā, after giving elaborate instructions for meditation, suddenly reveals the essence of meditation: "Don't think anything!" There lies the problem.

Try this exercise. Grind your whole thought process to a standstill by using one thought, 'I will not think,' like a broom, and sweep all other thoughts out with it. This is not meditation, but merely sitting and thinking 'I will not think'. Do this for a few minutes, then let go. Let the mind think what it likes for a couple of minutes, then begin again. You will see the fun.

You may find as many methods for meditation or for concentration or for entering into samāḍhi as there are teachers in the world, because meditation is not a technique which can be taught, but an experience which can be caught by each one in his own unique way. Having learned these methods, when you go into your own meditation room you will find you will still have to evolve your own method. What is good for another person may not be good for you. After studying everything on earth, eventually you will have to discover for yourself how not to think.

In the pursuit there are three types of internal obstacles. One – thinking itself. Streams of thought occur in the mind. From where do they come? Two – what are known as emotions. These emotions are a bit more problematic than mere thoughts. You will find that when there is a thought you are able to observe the thought fairly dispassionately; but when there is an emotion, it carries you off. E-motion is a motion outward. Three – the manifestation of energy (restlessness). You cannot pinpoint it as a thought or a feeling; it is just an amorphous disturbance of energy. You will have to discover it yourself, a description will not help.

The yogis have simplified our approach to these three, but unless we come face to face with them in ourselves this simplification is useless. The theory is that thought has its seat in the brain; emotion has its seat in the heart; energy has its seat in the solar plexus. If you have a bee buzzing in your bonnet it means your mind is focused too much on your head – shift it. If you are going crazy with some emotion, your whole attention is focused on your heart – shift it. There seems to be a simple method for doing this. In the case of both mental and emotional upheaval, try to see if you can shift your attention to the solar plexus. Then you have withdrawn the energy from the thinking and from the emotion and you are in contact with the energy centre. From there you are looking at the emotion or the thought. When you are looking at the emotion in this manner it does not move outside anymore. The emotional disturbance or mental disturbance is checked, and you have acquired some ability to look within yourself. Each one has to do it for himself – one cannot explain it too much.

You will discover that emotion is nothing more than thought of a different intensity of energy, a greater voltage. Thought is made of energy. The brain cells generate a minute electrical charge. That means prāṇa moves in the brain cells and they produce this thought. But that is not all, there is a second element to it. In those brain cells are hidden some past impressions. That is what you call memory. When this energy moves among those impressions something comes up, and this is what you call thought. This understanding helps you by revolutionising your observation. You are no longer caught up in these emotions, but are merely an observer. You see that energy activating brain cells produces thought, energy activating latent impressions produces thought. Thus you become free of your thoughts and your emotions.

In the Yoga Sutras, a beautiful series of meditation exercises is given. *vitarka vicārā nandā 'smitā 'nugamāt sampra jñātaḥ* – in-which a kind of path is carved out.

First *viṭarka:* you allow the mind to indulge in thinking thoughts and counter-thoughts. Then you look directly within to see where thought arises. Can you distinguish that spot where the thought arises? Is there any difference in the source, in the ground of the experiences, of pleasure and pain, of happiness and unhappiness? Are they not all different waves that are the one ocean?

That intelligence which sees this directly is called *vicāra.* Vicāra is not analysis or enquiry. It is when this awareness moves directly within to see that all these thoughts, all these feelings, are of the same substance, whether called pleasant or unpleasant, pleasure or pain, happiness or unhappiness.

The aggregate of all these is what we have so far considered as ' me' . The ' me' is, therefore, the ground of all these. When thus the ground of thoughts, feelings and experiences is directly seen, there is peace, not unlike the experience of sleep in which, however, there is still this ' I' .

We started by seeing differences in this world, good and evil etc. Then these seem to disappear because we realise that all these divisions were in ' me' , created by ' me' . Finally there is just ' me' left. But the ' me' , so long as it is there is capable of creating a division. Why do we run after what is called pleasure? Because we have given them a lot of value. Switch off this attraction/repulsion and the mind naturally moves in one area called 'god'. That is brahmacharya, which means the mind moves in Brahman. But although the object seems to have gone the ' I' is still there.

You look at a mountain and even though the idea that it is a mountain may not arise there is still the feeling: 'I see . . . . ' When the eyes are open there is seeing. What is it that jumps up within you and says: "I see"?

There is a lovely sutra in the Yoga Sutras which says: "The seen is the seeing." With this realisation there is great delight within you. There your enquiry ends. Then Divine Grace steps in; for the undivided intelligence or cosmic consciousness cannot be realised by the finite, by divided consciousness. ' I' cannot see God. ' I' cannot see the totality.

All this is part of what we call meditation. Meditation is self-discovery; it leads to self-knowledge which is synonymous with samāḍhi, enlightenment, freedom, liberation, etc. We readily understand what is meant by knowledge: it is knowledge of another, of an object. But self is not an object; self-knowledge is not knowledge of another. Hence, self-knowledge poses a big problem. All other knowledge is associated with thought; hence, self knowledge is said to be free of thought, a direct realisation. Self-knowledge is free of interference of the mind, hence it is declared that it follows control of the mind – though that is an extremely inadequate term.

There is a very big difference between our physical and psychological being. In the case of the body, exercise or work brings on fatigue. In the case of the mind, if it does not do anything, there is fatigue. If you make the mind stop functioning you will feel as though you are carrying a terribly heavy load, you are so fatigued. So we should neither stop the mind, nor let the mind flow as it will, but bring it under the control of our intelligence so that we may be able to observe it. It is possible to vary the technique, vary the method, but not the goal. Instead of sitting upright and meditating, one can walk about and meditate. Instead of inactively and passively sitting in your own meditation room or on the seashore, one can be active and meditating. Instead of outwardly seeming to be in the meditative mood, one can even go into a club or a hotel or a theatre, sit and listen to some music, and at the same time inwardly be watchful. One can do all sorts of things if one is sincere.

The whole problem of yoga or meditation is one of sincerity. If you are sincere you will find some way out. If not, nothing in the world will be of any use. Here one must use common sense all the time and modify the method of meditation to bring it in alignment with life itself, and bring life in alignment with our attempts at meditation. Our daily life and our meditative life should not be in conflict with each other, other wise there is no meditation at all. Everyone must constantly be watchful and alert.

50. THE I–DEA OF I

Such watchfulness or alertness itself generates virtue and order in one's life. It harmonises what is initially called the daily secular life and what is practised as yoga or meditation. This division of life is also the work of the ego, which pretends to holiness while clinging to unholiness. All division is ego; and evil and unwisdom flow from the ego.

Commonsense tells us that east and west, above and below, right and left, meet in 'me'. When you stand on the ground, all that lies in one direction is to the east and all that lies in the other direction is to the west; if you move a mile in the easterly direction, what you previously considered east has joined the west! Is it difficult then to see that you are not only the meeting point but you are also the dividing factor?

Caught in this trap of 'I am this' or 'I am that' we are not aware that there is a state of peace of mind, an existence that is unconditioned. Every time we want to get out of one trap, we walk into another trap. This is so because we have no idea whatsoever that a state beyond all this exists.

In yoga, at the beginning of our practice, it has to be taken for granted that there is a state of consciousness, accessible to all of us provided we are willing to take the necessary steps, in which there is no confusion, conflict, distress or disharmony, – a state of bliss, joy and peace which is reached through yoga, through meditation, through the understanding of the mind and its modifications (citta and vṛtti).

When you are not in that state of yoga, then the state of your mind, the thought and the feelings that prevail in it, determine the world around you. An object does not exist except as the sum total of all the thoughts of all the observers. When all these thoughts and viewpoints, opinions and descriptions are dropped, the object is what it is, not as an object anymore.

These are words. It is when you become like little children, as Christ enjoined, that you can get an idea of this. Hence, the Bhāgavathaṁ declares that the greatest sages are like little children. If you wish to learn to meditate the only person to teach you is a baby less than six weeks old. When you look into its eyes, you will know what yoga means. There it is in all its absolute purity, gazing at you without projecting a single thought of what you are!

Patanjali gives us a three-word phrase about yoga in his Yoga Sutras: *yogaś citta vṛtti nirodhah* (yoga is *citta vṛtti nirodha).* These three words cannot easily be translated into English.

What is citta? Mindstuff. This citta throws up countless vrittis (explained later). Something has to be done with these citta vṛittis to bring about a condition of yoga. That something is nirodha.

We want to know exactly what citta is, what mind is. Let us say that you have your eyes open and see something sitting in front of you, and a thought arises in you, 'He is a swami'. Someone else may think, 'He is a man' or 'He is an Indian' or 'He is a nice man' or 'He is not a nice man' and so on. How does all this happen? A totally blind man would not see a swami. What makes you see? Your eyes, the optic nerve and the particular brain centre. But in the optic nerve brain complex there is no swami, but merely light waves, vibrations. Where and how are these sensations or vibrations decoded into, 'He is a swami'? The material of which the sensations in their essential nature are made is citta.

All these are words. Citta cannot be grasped by your mind however brilliant you are. In order to know the ciṭṭa, you must experience it here and now. It must be as real as the ant crawling on your back, felt externally, or the headache or anger experienced internally. Seeing the chair is the perception of a material object. Being aware of the crawling of the ant on the back is a sensation, and the feeling of anger is an emotion. In one or all of these contexts, the ciṭṭa must become visible to you. You must *experience* it here and now. Just as you cannot experience a headache that is not there in you now, you cannot meditate unless there is meditation, you cannot know the citta unless the citta reveals itself to you. This will happen only when the vrttis make life intolerable, when all your desires and cravings begin to hurt you and the mind naturally turns upon itself.

Citta can only be experienced when desire naturally drops away. Only when it hurts will the mind let fall what we have been calling evil—the cravings, lust, the greed and hatred. You do not have to drop them at all. When you have developed sensitivity within yourself, then, without any outside persuasion, the mind is ready to let them drop. Then the citta is seen, is experienced. That is called meditation. Meditation is coming face to face with citta. In that state of yoga there is an inner understanding of the vrttis and the citta. Such understanding is nirodha.

Nirodha cannot be adequately translated. You look at the ocean and you look at the waves. Now there seems to be within you, a notion that the waves are something apart, something which come into being, which seem to exist, and dissolve in the ocean. You are creating a distinction, a division that is untrue, false. I am not suggesting that the wave is false, but the division that thought creates between the wave and the ocean is false. An enlightened person looks at the same ocean and he has the same vision, but in that vision there is no division. There is direct experience without the division created by the thought 'The wave has come out of the ocean' . Nirodha is the abolition of the non-existent division. The distinction between the wave and the ocean is only an idea. Let that disappear. Its disappearance is called nirodha.

Similarly, you have various ideas concerning the world and the objects around you. You need not suppress your thoughts, or express your thoughts; you need not run away from the world or get drowned in it; you need not wipe the world out of your vision—but you should directly see the truth and abandon the idea that you have concerning this truth.

In reality the citta is undivided, indivisible. Not only indivisible in the sense that there is no distinction between subconscious, conscious and superconscious in what is called the 'me', but in the sense that consciousness is cosmic all the time. Cosmic consciousness is indivisible. There is no such thing as my consciousness as distinct from your consciousness. The citta is really not restricted to the individual body.

If you compare citta to an ocean, each individual is just a ripple, a wave, in that ocean. Having continually identified yourself with one ripple, you consider yourself a limited individual (and you think that that individual is the whole). This individuation is what has brought about trouble, and it is the identification with the vrtti that has caused the individuation.

You can probably study these vrttis more closely and thoroughly within yourself, but one must never make the mistake of considering the cosmic intelligence to be limited to the individual. It is universal, yet it is easily accessible to each one within himself, within what he has come to regard as his self.

If you observe your own citta, you realise that vrittis (thought-waves, ideas) arise in it constantly, in that part of the citta where the attention is focussed. Some of these thoughts or ideas are considered pleasant and others unpleasant. The pleasant are pleasant because you like them (and of course you like them because they are pleasant!) and the unpleasant are unpleasant because you dislike them (and of course you dislike them because they are unpleasant). Regardless of whether they are considered pleasant or unpleasant, good or evil, ugly or beautiful, they are all thoughts and ideas, vrttis.

The observing intelligence is obscured by these vrttis and then there is the notion of an observer, the self or the ego.

What yoga philosophy suggests, if one studies it without preconceived notions and prejudices, is this. When you observe the ego, it is possible that you discover that the ego is not an entity like a table or a tape-recorder. The ego is more like an assembly in the sense that Buddha used that word. What you call consciousness, the self, is nothing but an assembly of past impressions and experiences. Buddha did not deny the existence of the world and its objects.

A great Buddhist used the example of the bullock-cart. He asked a disciple, "What do you see there?" as a cart drawn by bullocks passed. "A bullock cart." "What are those two circular things?" "Wheels." "Burn them." "Now what is sticking out there?" "The axle." "Throw it away." Then the body was discarded, then the yoke. "Where is the cart now?" If all the different parts that have their own name and individuality have been dismantled where and what exactly is the cart? If you put all these separate parts into a scrapheap , they would not make a cart. The cart is an idea. Even before the assembly of the parts, the idea of the cart was there and it persists.

The ego, the ' I' is nothing but an idea, a vṛṭṭi. As an idea ' I' exists, but not as an independent entity capable of producing its own ideas. One must observe all this. As you observe for instance, seeing, you note that seeing takes place. Who sees? The eyes see. While seeing happens, from somewhere, for no apparent reason, the idea arises, "I am seeing."

Patanjali gives us a very beautiful sutra in which there is a description of what is the ultimate in yoga. Translated literally, it reads: ' Then the seer rests in himself.' When you are not in that state of yoga, you identify yourself with a million thought waves or modifications of the mind. But ' in a state of yoga the seer rests in himself.' What does the seer signify? Later in the text we get an inspiring statement. "What one calls the seer is only *seeing.*" Why must you invent a thing known as ' I' which sees? When the eyes are open, they see. You have a beautiful expression in English, viz. ' sight-seeing tours.' The sight is what sees! Who sees the scenery? Sight sees. What you call the seer is nothing but the action, the event of seeing. All our yoga practices lead us to this realisation that seeing is not the doing of ' I' but a happening.

In exactly the same way, all of life can be lived. Sight sees, action takes place, everything in this world happens. Somehow, somewhere we have been conditioned by the idea that without this vanity, this ego, without a goal to reach and hold on to we shall not progress but our lives would be a failure. There is only one failure, the failure to do, not the failure to achieve. Success is always there. To succeed is ' to come after'. When one does anything, success follows. It is when you do not do what should be done there is failure.

Once you see the whole picture, action is spontaneous. The finite thing (I, you, he) does not exist in reality. It is only when you are not really spiritually awake that there is this division and confusion. Once the awakening has taken place, it stays alert until you discover the reality, and it swallows the 'I'.

As we have seen, citta is indivisible cosmic consciousness or intelligence, and the vrttis are ideas which may be knowledge, wrong understanding, imagination, memory or sleep. These are all universal—wherever there is ocean there are waves, wherever there is citta there are vrittis. It seems to be clear, but . . . . when you view the ocean as one indivisible entity, there are no waves *apart* from it. The whole thing, with all the waves, *is* the ocean.

Similarly, in the physical body there are millions of cells sparking off, all sorts of streams flowing from the heart to the parts of the body and back again, there is tremendous activity, yet because the organism *is* the activity, and there is no division, it is unaware of it. A body approaching fire is burned, but if you are the burning fire you will not be burned at all. You are the burn*er*, not the burn*ed*. Somehow this fact that 'I am that,' has been forgotten.

We ask, "Why should that cosmic intelligence forget that it is cosmic and create a diversity, change, or a becoming?" Why should this great universal being become anything? No one can answer. One can only bluntly, frankly and honestly say, "Sorry, I do not know."

Somehow, mysteriously there is what philisophers call māya or aviḍyā (translated as ignorance), which merely means, "I have no idea." But the question still remains as to how there can be ignorance in cosmic intelligence. This question is unanswerable. The same question comes round in countless different ways for us.

The body of everyone is made of the same substance. For all of us food comes from the same source, the earth. Prāṇa, the life force, is cosmic. We are all breathing the same air. We all have the same intelligence within us. It cannot be divided. Yet when someone calls you a fool, you become angry. But, when you say, "My hand is dirty", the hand does not strike the tongue for this remark. Yet this is what we do to one another. Somebody insults you and at once you want to retaliate. We eat the same food, but each one wants to destroy the other because "I feel that I am different from him."

How does this happen? We have missed two steps: we have forgotten that we are all one. And when this is forgotten there is a peculiar polarization–'I' and 'the other'. Neither cosmic intelligence nor cosmic ignorance (aviḍyā) creates the concept, the idea of you and me. It is in the shadow of aviḍyā that the 'I' arises and this 'I' creates 'you' and 'the other'.

Perhaps the first person pronoun 'I' is nothing but the abbreviation of the full word ' idea' . The 'I' may itself be nothing more than an idea. However, as soon as this idea arises, it creates you, the other person, then he, she and it.

The problem of our world is that the human being, the individual, each 'I' becomes the centre of the universe as soon as the ego-sense arises. Why do two individuals fight? Because each one assumes that he is the centre and that everything must somehow be related to his pleasure, to his will. This self-limited cosmic being, which is the individual personality, then goes on building relationships. It is all ignorance. The child and the grandchild of ignorance can only be ignorance, just as all offspring of man can only be human. So everything which manifests within this cosmic being or cosmic consciousness is born of ignorance. The self-limited infinite which is called the individual, looks around, feels, registers and reacts. Fear, contempt, like, dislike, attraction, repulsion, approval, disapproval—all these spring from the ignorant self-limitation that is called ego.

Once the idea of 'I' is there it becomes the centre of the entire universe. Who determines what is East and what is West? The deciding factor is where you stand at the moment. You lay down the law, as a nation or as a culture. It depends on where you stand physically, psychologically, morally or spiritually. 'We' declare this to be good and that to be bad, that is pleasant and this is not pleasant. The centre of creation is always 'I' and collectively 'we'.

From this 'I' comes rāga (attraction, approval or liking) and dvesa (repulsion, rejection or dislike). Rāga is better translated as 'approval' and dveṣa as 'disapproval'. If someone gently scratches your back you approve of him, but if he twists your arm, you disapprove of him. This is so because you see yourself as the centre of the universe.

There is one more category which the wise, keenly observant mind of the author of the Yoga Sutras recognised—a man clinging to one's physical life (or I would like to regard this as 'hope'). This clinging to life that is known to be temporary, which is found even amongst the wisest, absurd though it seems is a trend away from the centre, away from the cosmic intelligence. This trend is manifest in our lives as 'hope'—hope which is always related to the non-existent future, hope of even an after-life, heaven and so on.

How does one get over all this? How can one restrain all these innumerable thought-waves or ideas or notions with which one identifies oneself, because of one's original identification with one idea, the 'I'dea? How does one return to the source, the truth, the reality of one indivisible consciousness?

Patanjali says that the answer is abhyāsa and vairāgya. Abhyāsa means ' to be established in it' . All effort directed towards remaining established in the truth is abhyāsa. So abhyāsa means, in one word, practice. The sutra concerning vairāgya is somewhat complicated. It refers to objects seen and heard; longing for them is rāga and the cessation of such longing is vairāgya. There is vairāgya when the craving is turned upon itself–when there is intense craving only to know ' what the craving is' as soon as it arises.

Although I have described abhyāsa and vairāgya as two separate steps, they really go together. They are two sides of the same coin. A holy man gave a remarkably simple definition of the two words abhyāsa and vairāgya. "To know that cosmic consciousness alone is true–is abhyāsa; not to allow an idea of diversity ever to arise is vairāgya." Yoga does not restrict you to a set of practices; whatever enables you to be established in this cosmic consciousness is abhyāsa, provided you persist in that practice. Abhyāsa requires the integration of your entire life. This is similar to the Hassidic teaching that one's whole life should be offered to God, given a God-ward direction. If that is not there, then there is no abhyāsa, no practice.

Abhyāsa has to be combined with vairāgya. What is called vairāgya is extremely difficult to define, because all the definitions pre-suppose the opposite. Detachment implies having been attached. Vairāgya is not that. It is not dislike, or indifference. It is not aversion, or infatuation. If during yoga practice, there is a soft towel under you, the back of the neck ' likes' it. If there is a rough mat, the neck does not ' like' it. This approval or disapproval belongs not to ' me' , but to the body. The skin responds positively to a pleasant sea breeze and negatively to ice cold wind or desert heat. That is understandable, natural. But when you say, "I love him" or "I hate him" that is not natural. It does not exist in nature, but is a perversion of nature.

When you begin to see this, then your heart, mind or consciousness does not register the causative factors of rāga-dveṣa, whatever caused the attraction or aversion. That state in which your consciousness does not register these causes at all is vairāgya. There is no more registration of experiences. Let life flow on. The sensations, the body, the life-force, approve of certain things and disapprove of others. Let your consciousness not be tainted by this. If your finger intentionally or unintentionally pokes your eye there is no accusation, because the finger and the eye belong to the same organism. There is no aversion, no hatred against the finger. When the hand drives away a mosquito sitting on the cheek, there is no special love relation between the hand and the cheek as a result. These things go on naturally. The inner consciousness is not modified at all by these experiences. There is no judging, no condemnation, and therefore, no need to forgive and forget.

How does one overcome the mad clinging to life, the desire to live—hope? Krishna expands this idea in the Gita. The first need is to perceive immediately that all life is tainted by old age, sickness and death. This does not mean that one should not eat or marry and stop doing this or that. But when this immediate, direct perception is there constantly, then one's consciousness is not influenced by those experiences called pleasure and pain. It no longer runs after pleasure because it knows that it is temporary, not real. It will not masochistically look for pain. Pain and pleasure are inherent in life—there is no need to search for some more. When all desires re-enter oneself, return to the source, there is true vairagya, true dispassion—the total opposite of passion and craving.

The teaching of Patanjali points out that there is this cosmic being, cosmic oneness, cosmic harmony, cosmic consciousness, which has been mysteriously ruptured, fractured by ego-sense. The ego-sense says, "This is I", therefore "That is you". From this division flows an interminable stream of worry, anxiety, fear and hate. How does one put an end to this? By realising that you *are* the stream. The moment you realise that, the menace has ceased. The 'I am anxious' duality creates a distinction between 'I' and the anxiety. If you know that "I *am* anxiety", anxiety no longer haunts you. You are it, and there is no more struggle. The anxiety as anxiety falls away.

A very holy man pointed out, "Fear is the first product of duality. The realisation of non-duality, is yoga. But you cannot *create* harmony, bring about unity, or non-duality; there is no need, no possibility of this. It is already there. But what you can and must do is observe how and where this oneness has been disrupted. If one sincerely and seriously carries out this observation, then it does not take a split second to realise that the break happens the moment the 'I' thought arises. The moment the feeling "I am this" comes up, that thought, the vṛtti, mental modification creates the "you". and there is conflict.

Meditation is the direct observation of the arising of the 'I', the ego, without a mediator. A mediator is merely another distraction. Even words, descriptions of meditation, may be disastrous. Meditation is observation without descriptions of any type that will give you an image of what it 'should be.' What you practise while you are seated in a meditation posture is meant as a help. But even while talking, eating, looking at or doing anything, one should watch the arising of the 'I'. This questioning is to be done continuously, not only in the morning and evening. If we continually observe the arising of the ego-sense during our waking hours, whatever we are doing, then even while dreaming there is the enquiry, "Who is dreaming, to whom is the dream occurring?" So eventually even while one sleeps, there is this continuing self-consciousness. This continuous awareness which runs through all states of consciousness is called samadhi, the fourth state of consciousness.

But all these words are useless for us. So we are given exercises to lead us on to the discovery of the ego. When one is able to see where the 'I' thought comes from, one immediately realises, "Ah, this is the mischief-maker, this is the villain that has brought about a division, disrupted the harmony that in fact exists all the time." You observe where this fracture has occurred. You see that it is the 'I' that creates this disruption of harmony and as soon as the 'I' consciousness yields its place and reveals that it is merely a shadow, there is realisation of oneness.

51. THE EIGHT LIMBS OF YOGA

'I' makes the division, 'I' makes the disorder and thus 'I' is responsible for evil in this world. To preserve all this and yet to strive for meditation or to pretend to meditate is self-deception.

How does one get rid of this disorder, this evil and this sinful nature? Bhagavān Ramana Maharishi advocated the method of enquiry to trace all these evils to their single source – the ego – which when investigated further in what is known as vicāra, proves to be unreal. A devotee once asked him, "This method seems to be quicker than the usual one of cultivating qualities alleged necessary for salvation." Ramana answered: "Yes, all bad qualities centre round the ego. When the ego is gone realisation results by itself. There are neither good nor bad qualities in the self. The self is free from all qualities. Qualities pertain to the mind only."

The nature of life in which there is order and in which there is not the division of the ego-sense, has been mapped out and charted in the yoga text of Maharishi Patanjali under the headings 'yama' and 'niyama'.

Yama is five fold:

i. Non-violence (ahiṁsā)
ii. Adherence to truth (satyaṁ)
iii. Non-stealing (asteyaṁ)
iv. Continence (brahmacaryaṁ)
v. Non-coveting (aparigrahaṁ)

Swami Sivananda emphatically declares that ahiṁsā means positive love towards all beings. But we should not mistake this divine love for the manifestation of lust, with which this sublime emotion of love is universally confused. Hence Patanjali's cautious negative description. This love is not infatuation, attachment or lust; it is pure and divine, selfless, cosmic and self-sacrificing. This is a great truth which should not be forgotten.

Satyaṁ or truthfulness has elsewhere been defined as that which is at the same time pleasant and beneficial. Our speech should be truthful, pleasant and beneficial. Where these three criteria are not fulfilled, we should be silent.

Why has non-stealing been given a place of prominence among these great canons? The secret is revealed in the universal scripture, the Bhagavad Gītā. Lord Krishna calls him a thief who appropriates to himself all the gifts of the gods without sharing them with others. My master lays the greatest emphasis on this: "Give,

give, give. Share what you have with others," is his clarion call. That is what is alluded to by the word 'non-stealing' here.

Brahmacarya is generally translated 'continence' in connection with yama. Let us turn to Bhagavān Ramana Maharishi. A devotee asked him, "Is not brahmacarya (celibacy) necessary for the realisation of the self?" and the Maharishi replied: "Brahmacarya is 'living in Brahman'. It has no connection with celibacy as commonly understood. A real brahmachari (that is, one who lives in Brahman) finds bliss in the Brahman which is the same as the self. Why then should you look for other sources of happiness? In fact the emergence from the self has been the cause of all the misery." To a further question, "Can a married man realise the self?" the Maharishi replied, "Certainly, it is a matter of fitness of mind." Surely, then, continence should happen as a consequence of 'living in Brahman' or the consciousness flowing in a single stream towards the self; forced restraint is force and not restraint and besides negating the definition of brahmacarya, violates ahiṁsā, too! However, when it naturally happens, it makes available a great source of creative energy.

Aparigraha, or non-acceptance of what belongs to others, saves us from our own greediness. It acts as a curb on desires. It generates contentment, the axe which cuts at the root of a sense of want, the enslaving lust for material possessions which only oppress us by their weight, and pin us down to this earth.

Let us proceed to the next limb: Niyama. They are rules of conduct that govern our daily life.

Niyama is fivefold, too:

i. Cleanliness (śauca)
ii. Contentment (santoṣa)
iii. Austerity (tapas)
iv. Study (svādhyāya)
v. Devotion to god (īsvarapranidhanā)

All-round cleanliness is indicated by śauca. Cleanliness of the surroundings, of the clothes, of the body and of the mind and the heart. 'Cleanliness is next to godliness' is an accepted maxim. The prayerful devotee and the practitioner of yoga know that the mind tends to be pure and powerful in a clean body, in clean surroundings. Santoṣa is contentment, cheerfulness, acceptance of what falls to our lot without wry-faced grumbling. This enables us to be in a positive frame of mind, always up and doing, striving to steady the mind, free from distracting thoughts and desires and their opposite counter-thoughts and frustrations. Tapas or austerity is the twin sister of contentment. These two together bring about simple living and high thinking. "Simplify your life; purify your heart; intensify your sādhanā and meditation," are Swami Sivananda's teachings. We cannot serve god and mammon at the same time. If we multiply our wants, suffer from luxury, our mind will be where our heart is – in our earthly possessions – and it will be almost impossible to practise concentration and meditation. An austere and simple life is indispensable for yoga. In the Bhagavad Gītā Krishna has given a revolutionary definition of tapas. He calls for strict discipline of thought, word and deed. The aim is to awaken us from the earth-earthliness and to inspire us to keep the ideal of yoga always before us. Then comes svādhyāya, or study of scriptures, whose place in spiritual life cannot be overemphasised. Scriptures and the words of our own preceptor (or the guru) are the two eyes with which alone we can see our way. Finally īsvarapranidhāna or devotion to god, without whose grace no spiritual progress is possible. It is when we recognise this truth and surrender our finite little ego to him in prayerful devotion, that this subtle veil is removed and we are enabled to perceive the divinity that we are in truth.

My master Swami Sivananda does not want us to wait until we are established in these virtues before attempting the advanced yoga practices. He asks us to strive to concentrate and meditate, at the same time endeavouring to cultivate these virtues. The destination is brought nearer our reach.

The third limb is āsana – a steady and comfortable posture in which we can sit for a considerable time; a posture which enables us to forget the body without lulling us to sleep. Students of yoga all over the world have found padmāsana to be the best. Patanjali says that when you are able to sit steadily in this posture in a meditative mood, you 'overcome duality'. This is usually interpreted to mean pain and pleasure etc., but it may also indicate the overcoming of the sense of duality, which is possible only if the ego-sense ceases. The cessation of the ego-sense is the central issue.

After the body has thus been brought under control, we proceed to the next step. We have already seen that there is an intimate relation between the breath and the mind. When we are deeply thinking, when the mind is automatically concentrated, our breathing is slow, rhythmic and steady. When we suffer from that temporary madness of anger or lust, when our mind is agitated, we breathe hard, fast and haphazardly. Patanjali therefore prescribes control of breath or prāṇāyāma as the next step. Seated in padmāsana, we try to regulate the breath – inhalation, retention and exhalation. Do not forget the all-important criterion – slow, rhythmic, deep, graceful and steady breathing.

Even as this is being done we shall not fail to notice that the turbulent mind has become tame. There is an experience of peace, a foretaste of the transcendental experience which awaits us. We are ready to take the fifth step. Krishna asks us in the Gītā to withdraw our senses from their objects, just as a tortoiṣe withdraws its limbs into the shell. Our devotion to a personal deity helps us here. With closed eyes we perceive Him within us. Swami Sivananda exhorts us to repeat the mantra: our ears listen to this inner 'sound'. The senses are thus withdrawn from their contact with the external world. The mind longs to taste the peace and the bliss that await it in the inner realm. When the senses are turned inward, it is as if a million flashlights are focused into yourself. The light is brilliant. You are no longer interested in what goes on outside, but you are tremendously interested in what goes on inside. This is pratyāhāra.

If we have succeeded in all these we shall find the next one (the sixth limb) very easy. Ḍhāraṇā or concentration will be almost effortless, and effective. The mind of the common man knows only three states: it can either yield to a thousand distractions and roam about in the outer world (the waking state) or the inner world (the dream state), or it can succumb to inertia and ignorance (the deep-sleep state). The diligent practice of yama and niyama curb distractions. Āsana and prāṇāyāma drive away inertia. Now we are ready to experience the fourth or superconscious state. The rays of the mind are focused on itself. When they are passed through the lens of concentration (ḍhāraṇā) they burn the ignorance that covers the self or god-head in us. Ḍhāraṇā is defined by Patanjali as focusing the mind within. This is not because the omnipresent god is only within us, but because the omnipresence is realised most easily as the indwelling presence. A dissipated mind is unfit for this realisation.

By the grace of god we enter his presence, the kingdom of god within us. We roam that kingdom. We partake of the 'peace that passeth understanding' and the bliss that is perennial and unbroken. We drink at the fountain of immortality. This is ḍhyāna or meditation, the seventh limb of yoga.

In the light divine the little 'I' vanishes. In total self-forgetfulness we commune with the lord. The salt doll tries to measure the depth of the ocean: it gets dissolved. But it is the ocean of bliss in which we get so dissolved. This is samāḍhi, the eighth limb. We have successfully cut ourselves away from the trammels of this world of pain and death. The cords of ignorance and egoism that bound us to the relentless wheel of transmigration have been broken. The vicious octopus (ego-sense) which, with its tentacles of the pairs of opposites — like and dislikes, pain and pleasure, honour and dishonour, success and failure — was strangling us, is dead. This is known as kaivalya. This is the goal. The yogi who has reached the goal is once and for all liberated from sorrow: he swims in the ocean of bliss, he drinks at the fountain of peace and immortality.

It is important to understand both samāḍhi and kaivalya correctly. When during meditation THAT alone is (in other words, when the meditator has ceased to be a spectator and the truth or the consciousness alone exists) it is samāḍhi. It is the 'I' that creates the duality in all this, even up to the division of the meditator and meḍitation. In samāḍhi even this distinction disappears. Meditation which is non-different from consciousness alone is: the ego-sense which is non-different from it is now really so, having abandoned its unreal duality. That alone (all-one) is: that is kaivalya.

The path is strewn with psychic powers. Dhāranā-ḍhyāna-samāḍhi (together called saṁyama) can be applied to various objects of phenomena. The concentrated beam of light can be focused on anything, and that thing will reveal its true nature to us. But these powers are distractions and obstacles. The yogi should not be misled or waylaid by the spiritual bandits that these psychic powers are. With intense and unabated zeal, intense application and adamantine will, he should proceed direct to the goal, which is the realisation of cosmic consciousness or the indivisible intelligence. Merely visualising the divine presence and visualising oneself as being a cell in the cosmic body of god is not samāḍhi, it is visualisation. If this visualisation is intense it can appear to be and to materialise. That is not self-realisation.

Control of the senses and mind is the indispensable pre-requisite to successful meditation. Exciting and animal food, intoxicating drinks and drugs, amusements and pastimes that divert and distract the mind are all obstacles to be avoided.

Progress in meditation is rapid if you lead a well-regulated life and practise what my master called the yoga of synthesis. In your own daily life combine haṭha yoga, bhakti yoga, karma yoga, rāja yoga and jñāna yoga. You will have integral development. Without god's and guru's grace you cannot enter into deep meditation; therefore, never give up japa and worship and devotion to and service of the guru. Maintain good health through the regular practice of some yoga āsanas and prāṇāyāma. Selflessness in all your activities is a touchstone of progress in meditation. If you experience the presence of god in all, you will naturally be filled with love and compassion for all.

Patanjali in his Yoga Sutras and Krishna in the Bhagavad Gītā prescribe two remedies for the waywardness of the mind: (i) persistent practice and (ii) giving up those pleasures and evil habits which show up during the meditation practice and which thus disturb the mind. Regularity, which is absolutely essential, will establish the habit.

If you forget why you are practising yoga, it is possible to amplify this abhyāsa (practice) and vairāgya (dispassion or uncolouredness) into a thousand divisions and sub-divisions, a thousand rules and their exceptions and amendments. If, however, you never lose sight of the main issue (which is the realisation of undivided consciousness) then abhyāsa can only mean being firmly established in the state of non-division; and vairāgya, which is its necessary correlate, is the prevention of the consciousness being coloured by the awareness of objectivity.

All these eight limbs of Aṣṭāṅga yoga have to be practised from day to day, from moment to moment. The whole of life must be meditation, one continuous self-observation. One who does this is a yogi. One who does this is free from the painful effect of the ego-sense. He may still use the word ' I' . He will still eat, work and live, but without ego-sense.

Yoga is that state in which there is no conflict, no anxiety, no fear, no false ' I' ' you' relationship, no approval, no disapproval.

That supreme state of bliss and peace, while yet still living, is what is meant by yoga.

Yoga welcomes you to tests its doctrines in your own inner laboratory and taste the delicious fruits it offers you.

52. *WHY MEDITATE?*

The basic problem in the world today seems to be that there is no interest in meditation as such. It is partly the fault of people who preach and do propaganda for meditation. When you want to spread the practice of meditation and encourage people to take it up, you persuade them that there is some benefit in it. In order to do that the preachers suggest, 'Practise meditation. You will be completely free of all tension.' The moment that aspect enters the field of meditation, the whole practice is ruined. From there on you are not sitting completely relaxed, meditating, but you are tense, looking at the state of relaxation which the preacher suggested was your goal. Trying to reach out to it you become more tense.

The moment you introduce a goal to meditation, it is gone. Happiness in life comes not by manipulating what you want to achieve but by paying attention to something seemingly totally unconnected with it. In order to make the mouth laugh, you tickle the foot. This seems to be of fundamental importance. Concentration of mind is not achieved by concentrating the mind, but by going right round doing something completely different. That is actually what the great masters of yoga suggested when they said to sit down and repeat your mantra.

The problem is that our minds are in a terrible state of disorder, our attention is not steady at all. Physically we are tense, mentally we are distracted. We go to a teacher and he says – "Sit down and repeat a mantra." While you pay attention to the mantra, which is totally unrelated and unconnected with the problem you are really trying to solve, the problem gets dissolved. You don't have to solve the problem, the problem can be dissolved. That is much simpler, otherwise when you have a problem and someone tells you to solve it, the solution becomes another problem! The confused brain creating another solution, is in worse confusion. The mind, after all, is one thing, not a supermarket. You are happy sometimes and you are unhappy sometimes. When you are unhappy, what happens to that happy person? And when you are happy, what happens to the unhappy person? Are you one or two? It is not difficult for you to see that you are one thing.

The mind is one substance which seems to assume several successively different disguises. It is not possible for the mind to be in two moods at the same time, and even when one is able to juggle the moods quickly, it only means that the mind is able to change very fast.

There is no more mystification about meditation than this. The master, by suggesting that you sit down and go on repeating a mantra, has made you temporarily forget your problem. A problem that is forgotten does not exist, unhappiness that is forgotten is happiness. It can come back again, but never mind. If you have been unhappy for 6 or 7 hours at a stretch, you have at least had 20 minutes of happiness. That is marvellous; the unhappiness was a mental state, nothing more than a mood.

In real life we see quite plainly that if an external situation was responsible for one's unhappiness, that situation is not going to be changed by being unhappy. Therefore the yogi said "Free yourself from this external compulsion and realise that unhappiness is a mental mood." The mind substance is still there, it has temporarily assumed the form of unhappiness, the character of unhappiness. You can be sure that even if you are in the worst of all moods now, the sun is not going to be veiled because of you, it will still shine brilliantly. And if you shake off your bad mood and get into the sun, it is to your advantage. You have been unhappy before, you may be unhappy later – 'so what'! All the problems are there waiting outside – let them! For the next half hour sit down and say your mantra, and as you go on in this way, suddenly you discover that the unhappiness is not there any more. Suddenly you realise that you (or something in you) is totally independent of the happiness or unhappiness that the environment imposes upon you. Coming out of your meditation room you are able to say 'so what', right in front of the unhappiness that faces you again.

So it is possible to free yourself psychologically from external compulsion, external imposition. Sitting there in that room for half an hour you have tasted it. The mind being of one substance was fed with this mantra, or something totally unconnected with all worries and anxieties, happiness and unhappiness.

You have not been struggling, you have not been praying to God to please take this problem away. (That is useless – another one will come.) But in the meantime you have discovered that it is possible for you, without changing the external environment, to be happy within yourself. You taste it. The most important thing in meditation is not to try to solve the outside problem, but to taste the present mood of peace and joy and happiness that is flowing inside. Then when you come out you are able to face this problem.

I am not saying the problems we are surrounded by can ever be removed, but the inner attitude can be radically and instantly changed. It doesn't even take half an hour. Meditation makes this possible by not dealing with the problem head on, but by turning the attention to something completely different (which happens to be beyond the source of all problems). This is not a policy of escapism. Let us take a very simple example of inter-personal conflict. You and he are working in the same organisation. You are saying something, he is saying something different, you have a little misunderstanding, a quarrel. He is too strong and powerful, so you don't want to fight with him. You go into your meditation room, sit and repeat the mantra. After a short while everything is at peace within yourself – there is harmony and joy within you. Are you escaping? No, because you have got to come out and meet him, again. Then you are a completely changed person, you realise that conflict can be ended by ending it within yourself. There is a lovely expression: "You cannot clap with one hand." It needs two to make a quarrel, they say, but I feel "It needs only one to make a quarrel – me".

The yogi's approach through meditation deals with the fundamental problem of human response. Once you have trained yourself in this technique (you can call it meditation or concentration) then it is possible for this to happen throughout the day, when there is need for you to respond. And though superficially it looks as if you are self-centred and selfish, you are not, because you have found the key to dissolving the problems and conflicts. That I think is the greatest contribution one can make to human happiness in society as a whole.

Half the problem connected with meditation springs from thinking about it. The thoughts that one may have about meditation are not meditation. It is possible to think about it, it is possible to talk about it and it is even possible to 'do' it, but none of these is meditation. Like sleep, it is something that has to happen, and one does not know when it is happening, but realises something has happened in retrospect. What is it that puts an end to sleep? What is it that puts an end to meditation? Strangely enough the desire to experience it.

We are trapped in a strange and delightful problem. We need to meditate but we cannot will ourselves into meditation. Meditation is vitally important not only to some of you who might be spiritual seekers, but also to people who want to become more alert in mind and in intellect, and even to people who pursue material goals. If meditation is a state in which there is no mental confusion, there is inner harmony and peace, then it is of vital importance to everybody. Whatever be your aspirations, whatever you are looking for – whether spiritual, intellectual, mental or material – one who knows what it is to meditate, or what it is to surrender oneself to meditation, realises that the key to any achievement is there. But fortunately or unfortunately, it is not possible to force it.

It is extremely fortunate that meditation cannot be made to happen, for the simple reason that if it could, it is liable to be marketed as we already see is being done, and what is even worse, it can be mis-used and abused. It is unfortunate because though we aspire for the state called meditation it seems to elude us and we are still groping. A few broad hints may be given, but even these are like preparing the bed as an invitation to sleep. You cannot 'go to sleep'. It is an expression as inadequate and erroneous as all expressions are. Sleep has to come – you can only go to bed.

53. *HOW TO MEDITATE*

So many textbooks are available on meditation nowadays that everyone has some idea of what it is all about. In brief, meditation is the most wonderful adventure: 'Discovery of self'. Meditation enables us to enjoy consciously the peace, happiness and revitalisation that we unconsciously have in sleep. Meditation lifts us above the cares and anxieties of our daily life, it enables us to overcome our moral weaknesses and evil habits and thus transform our very life. By dispelling ignorance, meditation removes all our morbid and childish fears and leads us to the hall of divine light, where we perceive our self as the immortal essence of all existence, where we realise that we are at once linked in a bond of eternal love with all creation. By enabling us to get in tune with this cosmic substratum and so with others, meditation gives us supernatural powers. Unless these powers (of whose existence we are not conscious and which we shall not deliberately use) become natural to us, they should be shunned as distractions.

'An ounce of practice is better than tons of theory' . The following simple procedure will in due course enable you to enjoy deep meditation

1. Select a calm, quiet, clean and secluded spot or a room or corner of a room in your house reserved for this purpose. Sit there (preferably facing east – the run rises in the east – or north

– there is a great power in the north pole), with a symbol of God or a lighted lamp or candle, placed at eye-level. The best posture is, of course, the lotus posture; if you cannot do this, sit in any comfortable posture with your body erect, as for the prāṇāyāma exercise discussed earlier. The yogi wants you to keep the back straight. All sorts of interesting reasons have been given, and one might be of interest to you. If the small of the back is held in, your back is naturally straighter than before. It seems to promote alertness of the mind. The moment you slouch and the small of the back shoots backwards and the spine curves forward your alertness is gone. The best time to meditate is from 4 to 6 a.m., but if this is not possible do this as soon as you wake up. It is good to have a quick bath; if this is not possible (without loss of the good morning hour), have a quick wash of hands, feet and face.

2. Chant a few hymns or offer your own prayer (audibly) to the lord: this is like switching the radio on and tuning it. Raise the mind to a higher level. Imagine you are in the presence of god. This may appear to be self-hypnotism, but the results are astounding.

3. Become aware that you are seated in your room or wherever it is. You are now aware of even your body's contact with the seat. The knowledge 'I am sitting here' ensures that the mind is also here and does not wander away. If the attention tends to wander, gently but firmly bring it back: 'I am sitting here.' Become aware of the sensation of the hands resting on your knees or in your lap. Immediately the attention is brought within the body and once the attention is narrowed down, the whole inside seems to be illuminated. You realise that just one thing is happening – breathing. You are breathing.

4. Chant 'oṁ' deeply, concentrating on the solar plexus, feeling that the sound vibrations arise from there. Feel that these sound vibrations travel upwards towards the crown of the head, through the vagus nerve. They actually will. When they reach the throat-region close your lips and continue ommmmmmm and let the sound fade out at the crown of the head. Do this three or six times.

5. It is one of those ironies of life that we seem to be interested in so many wonderful things in this world without paying the least attention to the greatest wonder which is breathing. It is because we are breathing that we are alive, that we are able to enjoy life. It is a supreme wonder. Ask yourself: "What makes you breathe out and having exhaled – what makes you inhale again?" What makes one take the next breath, or in other words, how does the breathing go on? When you pay attention to this you have forgotten where you are sitting. That is, the attention has gone still deeper within yourself and is now ready to go even deeper down. Breathe normally, effortlessly. At the same time, close the glottis a little bit, so that the breath itself produces some sound. (It is not the vocal cords but the glottis that helps to produce this sound.) Let this sound also fade away and not stop abruptly. You will find that your mind follows this sound and "goes inwards." You may do ujjāyī or bhrāmarī prāṇāyāma.

6. Breathe gently now. Watch the breath. Try to listen to it without producing any sound even with the throat. It is good to use a visualisation of the nāḍīs in conjunction with the breathing to bring about more intense concentration of the mind. Visualise the inhaled breath flowing down the iḍā and the piṅgalā nāḍīs on both sides of the spine. Hold the breath (kumbhaka) for just a moment. (Kumbhaka literally means 'pot-like', which alludes to the abdominal cavity being filled by the inhaled breath.) Visualise the exhaled breath ascending up the suṣuṁnā (the central channel), at the same time drawing the abdomen in and up, as in uḍḍīyāna bandha.

7. Now the only thing you are doing is breathing. That is the only action, motion, movement. Become aware of this. Let there be the inner awareness, "I am breathing," and let this stop the mind from doing something else. Gently but firmly hold on to the awareness, "I am breathing ".

8. Repeat your mantra (any name of god or sacred formula or 'oṁ') as you breathe in and out, without straining the breath. Associate the mantra with the breath – this is the trick. Repeat it once while you breathe in and once while you breathe out. If the mantra is long, repeat half while inhaling and the other half

while exhaling, without breaking it. Without tension you gently but actively keep listening to the mantra being heard within yourself. Become more and more deeply aware of this sound. Listen to it with all your heart, with all your attention.

9. Keep looking at the picture, symbol or the flame in front of you (that is what you have been doing all the time, at least from step 5 above) but transfer that symbol to within yourself. Feel that the image is in your own heart. See it there. Do not stare at the picture or flame in front; if you do, then your eyes will get tired and begin to smart. If you merely look without staring or focusing you will find that the symbol goes out of focus. Do not worry. Your eyes will not blink. They will not water or smart.

10. Now close your eyes if you like, and visualise that image of god clearly within your heart. Let it be radiant and living. If the mind tends to wander keep the eyes open, looking within.

11. Gradually let that image expand till it occupies your whole body, the room in which you are sitting and eventually the whole world. Feel this. Feel that you yourself are just a little part of god, one with him.

12. Sit like this for a minimum period of 20 minutes. (The preliminaries may take about 10 minutes.) Gradually increase this period.

13. After this period is over, offer a prayer to the lord for the health and long life of sick people (whom you can actually visualise in front of you) and the peace and prosperity of those who are suffering.

14. Get up slowly. Do not immediately run away. Take a few minutes before you leave the meditation room. Your mind and your nerves were extremely calm during this practice and if you suddenly jump out of that mood and rush into company, you might injure the nerves. This is very important.

15. You can practise this at other times, too – several

times a day. Do not sit for this practice within two hours after a meal. Do not wear tight clothing.

16. Do not eat anything for half an hour after this practice. And do not take bath immediately either.

17. If you wish to do a few rounds of prāṇāyāma, you may do so before you start this meditation practice or soon after step 2 above. Bhastrikā is useful.

If the mind wanders open your eyes, gaze at the picture and start all over again from step 5 above.

Japa (repetition of a mantra) itself will lead to meditation. The lord's grace will lead you to meditation and samāḍhi.

If evil thoughts enter the mind, do not pay any attention to them. Let them depart, as uninvited guests will if totally ignored! Go on with your japa, visualising the lord in the heart. If the mind wanders, resort to mental worship; or, open your eyes again and gaze at the image.

It is very important to see that the body and mind are relaxed. There should be no tension anywhere. The posture of the body should be steady but not tense. The mind should be concentrated on the object with ease: otherwise, every extraneous thought entering the mind will also get fixed there! Let go your hold on the world and gently hold on to the thought of god.

The secret in meditation is to be active without effort. Usually we are either active and full of effort or we go to sleep. But there is a state which is the happy medium between the two – to be awake and alert, but without struggle.

In the initial stages of meditation it is possible that as soon as the mind is concentrated and you begin to do japa, something you had forgotten is recollected by the mind. If it pertains to the business of the day, the mind is distracted. It is therefore advisable (in the initial stages) to keep a piece of paper and pencil by your side and note these down, so that the mind may be reassured that they will not be forgotten again and that it could go on with the japa. Use your commonsense in overcoming such obstacles.

Several methods have already been suggested not only to offset obstacles but to keep the meditation alive and alert. The very best is of course to seek the source of the sound of the mantra that is heard, and then the identity of the one that listens to the mantra. If this method is mastered,no disturbances (internal or external) need distract you, because you know how to make use of any disturbance! Anything that happens inside or around you is only going to stimulate you to greater vigilance. If there is a distraction, this vigilance will confront it with the question, "I am watching my breath and repeating the mantra. From where do you come?" Thus, there are no obstacles at all from there onwards.

On no account should you give up the morning meditation and get up from your seat before the appointed time: if the mind knows that you are a hard taskmaster, it will meekly obey you.

One of the main reasons why this meditation exercise is performed in the early morning hours is because it is then that the ego-sense arises after the period of deep sleep earlier. It is therefore possible to ask oneself: "Where was this ego-sense a few minutes ago? How does it arise and what is its source?"

Even during the day, close your eyes every hour and consciously withdraw the mind from the world, repeat the mantra and meditate upon god for just a few seconds. Keep up the current. If you keep a small japamālā (rosary) in your pocket, it will help.

By even attempting to practise meditation you will enjoy peace of mind and the ability to concentrate the mind at will wherever you are.

Another period of meditation just before going to bed is of incalculable benefit. It carries the fruits of meditation into the state of deep sleep. A great spiritual teacher said that if you restore order to the mind before you go to sleep, the mind is free to refresh itself thoroughly. Meditation restores order to the mind.

Of course all that has been described so far is no more

than japa or the repetition of a mantra and the visualisation of what that mantra represents. These are effective aids – but in themselves they do not constitute meditation. The use of these aids is based on a simple and sound principle. The world outside is mainly name-and-form to us: the other sense stimuli are not so strong as the visual and the auditory. Our waking consciousness is dominated by sights and sounds. Our inner world is even more so. Our dreams (day dreams as well as night dreams) are also made up of these two. Objectivity is name and form. Hence, the student of yoga replaces the multitude of names and forms (worldly, exciting, emotion-generating and pain-ridden) by one name and form of god (divine, sublime, peace-giving and bliss-filled). This too is name and form, and this too is an object – though surely god is not a name and form, and god is not an object. Ultimately therefore even this will go; but pushing it is foolishness.

Used rightly, however, these aids turn out to be valuable. And, what is their right use?

Patanjali's Yoga Sutras suggest the following:

When the name and the form are perfectly steady, the student begins to question it. "Is this the reality? Is this the self? Is this god? Is it not my own imagination, the object of my thought, the projection of my mental conditioning?" This questioning is not just mental or intellectual exercise; it is much deeper, for by this time the mind is fully concentrated, the image is clear and steady, and the mind is calm.

The answer to all these questions is an obvious 'yes'. However, the student does not abandon the whole thing and get up and walk away. He enters into himself even more deeply. The enquiry may continue along these lines: "This is not the self or the reality. But, then, what is it? How is the unuttered sound heard within: what is it made of? How do I see this image, where is it, and what is it made of?" Surely, there are no verbal answers to these questions! The sound is not made in the usual way (by the vocal cords, etc.). The image of god (or whatever it is that is chosen for the inner visualisation) is not there as a solid substance. What is it made of? 'The mind-stuff' is an unacceptable answer: it is an expression as meaningless as the other one we suggested to ourselves as an aid – 'god within'. To be meaningful it must be as real and as clear to you as this paper is. Thought answering a question concerning thought is waste of time. Hence, we pursue the enquiry by direct internal observation. The vital aspect of this part is to reject all thoughts concerning this phenomenon.

At this stage the observing consciousness looks steadily at the object. There is no movement of thought. There is great clarity. Suddenly it becomes clear that the object is but a reflection, a projection in the indivisible consciousness. Thus the division between the observer and the observed is abolished; and this gives rise to an experience of inner delight.

However, there is still movement in consciousness. Consciousness is still aware of itself: this is the original division which is therefore potential diversity. There is the awareness of 'I am' which can easily expand itself into 'I am this', 'I am that' etc. Hence, even this is known as samāḍhi with consciousness, or samāḍhi with the seed of diversification present.

Beyond this no effort on the part of the student is of any use, nor is it necessary. An effort is the expression of the ego, perpetuation of the division; abandonment of the effort is also the expression of the ego's inability or unwillingness to reach this point. The ego-sense should reach this point and in total self-surrender abandon all effort to abolish division, in the knowledge that the ego itself is the creator of the division, it is itself the division. What happens beyond this the masters have alluded to as 'divine grace'. Patanjali also speaks of god as what remains after the ordinary self-awareness ceases to be (puruṣa viśeṣah).

Awareness of division is the abolition of division. There is no division in the awareness which is undivided by the division. This position is not reached, it is not something to be attained: it is, it always is. When the dividing ego is seen to be incapable of dividing the indivisible, the shadow is seen as shadow; that which is is: it alone is – and that is kaivalya aloneness or all-one-ness, the knowledge that infinite diversity is infinite.

How this enlightenment takes place no one knows. At one moment this inner light begins to shine everywhere in your consciousness, and suddenly the 'I' has disappeared. It was not there in the first place. Only consciousness remains. Knowledge alone remains. Action alone remains. Seeing alone remains. Without the ego creating a division, a space between I and the other. When this light shines constantly within oneself, only then is one able to realise that what goes on inside is love; that that love is genuine and that that love is directed towards the omnipresence.

☆☆☆☆☆☆☆☆☆☆

Chapter Six

JÑĀNA YOGA

54. *SELF-KNOWLEDGE*

In support of all these practices, the Haṭha Yoga Pradīpikā declares: "There is no self-knowledge as long as there is the mind in motion; the mind does not cease to move as long as the prana moves. He who arrests the motion of the prāṇa and the mind attains liberation."

Bhagavān Ramana Maharishi approved of prāṇāyāma and encouraged seekers to practise it. However, he asks: "Is it the mind that wants to kill itself? The mind cannot kill itself. So your business is to find the real nature of the mind. Then you will know that there is no mind. When the self is sought, the mind is nowhere. Abiding in the self, one need not worry about the mind." That is meditation and samāḍhi in brief.

Again, the Maharishi made another thought provoking statement: "Both meditation and investigation amount to the same. Those unfit for investigation must practise meditation. In this practice the aspirant, forgetting himself, meditates 'I am Brahman' or 'I am Śiva'; thus he continues to hold on to Brahman or Śiva; this will ultimately lead to the residual being as Brahman or Śiva which he will realise to be pure being, i.e., the self. Meditation is possible only if the ego be kept up. There is the ego and the object meditated upon. The method is indirect. Whereas the self is only one. Seeking the ego, i.e., its source, ego disappears. What is left over is the self. The method is the direct one."

Though he had said that the self is only one, he adds

that even that as a concept is to be discarded. He says,"If there is unity, there will also be duality. The numeral 1 gives rise to other numbers. The truth is neither one nor two. It is as it is. Leave the thought-free state to itself. Do not think of it as pertaining to you. Just as when you walk you involuntarily take steps, so too in your actions: but the thought-free state is not affected by your actions."

All this is direct experience, not intellectual knowledge. It is beyond the ego, beyond division and therefore beyond thought and expression. Yet, even here the sages have evolved some aids.

Thus, jñāna (self-knowledge) is often classified into parokṣa jñāna (indirect, others'-eye wisdom) and aparokṣa jñāna, (direct, not-others'-eye wisdom). The former is acquired through books and teachers, who are extremely essential and indispensable, but who can lead us 'thus far and no further', who can only place the bread of wisdom on the table. We should consume it, digest it and assimilate it. Then it becomes aparokṣa jñāna. In this world, to give a rather gross and crude illustration, the knowledge that Mr. So-and-so is a man is indirect knowledge, but the knowledge "I am a man" is direct knowledge. Indirect knowledge is knowledge-by-acquaintance but direct knowledge is knowledge-by-identity. It is when bread is no longer bread but 'you' - assimilated (which means it has become similar to you). That is what vēḍānṭa literally means: 'end of knowledge', which is when knowledge ceases to be knowledge but it becomes 'you'.

However much we argue in favour of free-thinking, it is saner to admit that this freedom is always conditioned by tuition consciously or unconsciously received. This tuition stands in the way of intuition. To overcome this we need the guru. All the great masters have declared that as long as one seeks one needs a guide, that even though the real guru is within and this inner guru is the same as the lord and the self of each one, this inner guru appears as the external guru for the guidance of the aspirant.

The seeker approaches the guru in all humility and devotion (love). That is the only attitude in which reception of the spiritual truth is at all possible.

The first step at that stage is śravaṇa (hearing). It is

not acceptance yet. It is like the lunch laid out on the table, not yet served. It does not appease anyone's hunger.

The second step is manana (reflection). Reflection is just *that* sense of the word: the aspirant holds the teaching steadily in his mind so that it is clearly reflected in the mirror of his intelligence. This is like partaking of the lunch. Tradition allows even discussion and dialogues among the aspirants at this stage, to clarify the teaching.

The third step is niḍhiḍhyāsana (contemplation). Here the teaching is assimilated. It is the same as the samāḍhi of rājā yoga. There is enlightenment. The lunch is no longer food on the table nor chyme in the stomach, but flesh of your flesh, the bone of your bone – no longer food, but *you*.

It is the ruggedness of this path that prompted the sages who designated it to lay down the qualifications of the seekers who could pursue it. They are:

(a) viveka – or the inner light in which the shadow is seen as shadow and substance as substance. which in practice is

(b) vairāgya – which is the total absence of mental colouring or conditioning, and which is therefore the twin-sister of viveka: these two together ensure order in life, and in behaviour manifest as

(c) the sixfold virtue in the aspirant – namely, śama (control of the mind), dama (control of the senses), titikṣā (endurance), uparati (un-worldliness), śraddhā (faith) and samādhāna (equilibrium of the mind). All these are not golden shackles of proud virtue but based on

(d) mumukṣutva – or a keen longing for liberation from ignorance.

The aspirant who is endowed with these qualifications is benefited by the master's teaching. Enlightenment is dependent entirely on the intensity of the disciple's work.

What form the guru-disciple encounter takes from here on is individualistic: it is the upanishad, which literally means sitting near. It may take the form of a dialogue or a discourse. The guru may adopt one of the many methods of leading the disciple to enlightenment.

The following three dialogues from "Talks with Sri Ramana Maharishi," a treasure house of sparkling wisdom which every earnest aspirant must read daily illustrate this. Bhagavan Ramana Maharishi was one of the greatest and true modern representatives of the upanishadic sages.

I

Devotee: How is god to be seen?

Maharishi: Within. If the mind is turned inward god manifests as inner consciousness.

Devotee: God is in all – in all the objects we see around us. They say we should see god in all of them.

Maharishi: God is in all and in the seer. Where else can god be seen? He cannot be found outside. He should be felt within. To see the objects, mind is necessary. To conceive god in them is a mental operation. But that is not real. The consciousness within, purged of the mind, is felt as god.

Devotee: There are, say, beautiful colours. It is a pleasure to watch them. We can see god in them.

Maharishi: They are all mental conceptions.

Devotee: There are more than colours. I mentioned colours only for an example.

Maharishi: They are also similarly mental.

Devotee: There is the body also – the senses and the mind. The soul makes use of all these for knowing things.

Maharishi: The objects or feelings or thoughts are all mental conceptions. The mind rises after the rise of the I-thought or the ego. Wherefrom does the ego rise? From the abstract consciousness or pure intelligence.

Devotee: Is it the soul?

Maharishi: Soul, mind or ego are mere words. There are no entities of the kind. Consciousness is the only truth.

Devotee: Then that consciousness cannot give any pleasure.

Maharishi: Its nature is bliss. Bliss alone is. There is no enjoyer to enjoy pleasure. Enjoyer and joy – both merge in it.

Devotee: There are pleasure and pain in ordinary life. Should we not remain with only pleasure?

Maharishi: Pleasure consists in turning and keeping the mind within; pain in sending it outward. There is only pleasure. Absence of pleasure is called pain. One's nature is pleasure – bliss.

Devotee: Is it the soul?

Maharishi: Soul and god are only mental conceptions.

Devotee: Is god only a mental conception?

Maharishi: Yes. Do you think of god in sleep?

II

Devotee: How to realise the self?

Maharishi: The self is always directly perceived. There is no moment when it is not so. How then is it to be ascertained? Find out the self. You are that.

Devotee: But it is said the heart-knots are cut away and all doubts end when the supreme is found. The word dṛṣṭi is used.

Maharishi: To be the self is the same as seeing the self. There are no two selves for the one to see the other.

Devotee: How to realise the self?

Maharishi: It is already realised. One should know this simple fact. That is all.

Devotee: But I do not know it. How shall I know it?

Maharishi: Do you deny your existence?

Devotee: No, how can that be done?

Maharishi: Then the truth is admitted.

Devotee: Yet, I do not see. How shall I realise the self?

Maharishi: Find out who says, 'I'.

Devotee: Yes. I say 'I'.

Maharishi: Who is this 'I'? Is it the body or someone besides the body?

Devotee: It is not the body. It is someone besides it.

Maharishi: Find it out.

Devotee: I am unable to do it. How shall I find it?

Maharishi: You are now aware of the body. You were not aware of the body in deep sleep. Still you remained in sleep. After waking up you hold the body and say, "I cannot realise the self". Did you say so in your sleep? Because you were undivided then, you did not say so. Now that you are contracted within the limits of the body you say, "I have not realised". Why do you limit your self and then feel miserable? Be of your true nature and happy. You did not say 'I' in sleep. You say so now. Why? Because you hold to the body. Find out where from this 'I' comes. Then the self is realised.

III

Devotee: We do not understand how to realise. Can you help us towards realisation?

Maharishi: How do you meditate?

Devotee: I begin to ask myself 'Who am I?', eliminate body as not 'I', the breath as not 'I', the mind as not 'I', and I am not able to proceed further.

Maharishi: Well, that is so far as the intellect goes. Your process is only intellectual. Indeed, all the scriptures mention the process only to guide the seeker to know the Truth. The Truth cannot be directly pointed out. Hence this intellectual process. You see, the one who eliminates all the not-I cannot eliminate the 'I' To say 'I am not this' or 'I am that' there must be the 'I'. This 'I' is only the ego or the 'I'-thought. After the rising up of this 'I'-thought all other thoughts arise. The 'I'-thought is therefore the root-thought. If the root is pulled out all others are at the same time uprooted. Therefore seek the root 'I', question yourself 'Who am I?'; find out its source. Then all these will vanish and the pure self will remain forever.

Devotee: How to do it?

Maharishi: The 'I' is always there – in deep sleep, in dream and in wakefulness. The one in sleep is the same as that who now speaks. There is always the feeling of 'I'. Otherwise do you deny your existence? You do not. You say 'I am'. Find out who is.

Devotee: Even so, I do not understand. 'I', you say, is the wrong 'I' now. How to eliminate this wrong 'I'?

Maharishi: You need not eliminate the wrong 'I' – How can I eliminate itself? – All that you need do is to find out its origin and abide there. Your efforts can extend only thus far. Then the beyond will take care of itself. You are helpless there. No effort can reach it.

Devotee: If 'I' am always – here and now, why do I not feel so?

Maharishi: That is it. Who says it is not felt? Does the real 'I' say it or the false 'I'? Examine it. You will find it is the wrong 'I'. The wrong 'I' is the obstruction. It has to be removed in order that the true 'I' may not be hidden. The feeling that I have not realised is the obstruction to realisation. In fact it is already realised; there is nothing more to be realised. Otherwise, the realisation will be new; it has not existed so far, it must take place hereafter. What is born will also die. If realisation be not eternal it is not worth having. Therefore, what we seek is not that which must happen afresh. It is only that which is eternal but not now known due to obstruction; it is that we seek. All that we need do is to remove the obstruction.

IV

And, finally one last word from Sage Vāsiṣṭha. The following excerpt is from the Yoga Vasiṣṭha, Nirvāṇa Prakaraṇaṁ (part two) chapter 31: "The infinite consciousness reflects itself as the infinite and unconditioned consciousness in all and that alone is truly experienced in all. But when the notion of an object arises and when that notion is confirmed by repetition, this consciousness manifests as the object, like the dream-objects which, though within oneself, appear in that dream to be objects. When a dream-object perishes, nothing is lost: when the 'world' or the 'I' is lost, nothing is lost. There is no sense even in condemning this world and the egosense. Who will extol or condemn an hallucination? Investigation alone is appropriate here. What remains is the truth. Remain firmly established in it.

This world-appearance is but a notion and it is utterly dispelled by enquiry. What remains then is Brahman. To accept the reality of this world-appearance is like trusting the words of the barren woman's son. The individual personality is vāsana or mental conditioning which disappears on investigation. However, in a state of ignorance when one fails to observe it, this world-appearance arises.

The body is the result of the permutation and combination of the five elements and is inert. Even the mind, the intellect and the egosense are also of the same elements. When one is able to abandon the inert materiality of the mind, the intellect and the egosense, one attains the pure unconditioned being. This is liberation.

The 'object' arises in the 'subject' but has no independent existence. Hence, even 'the conditioned state or being' is but a notion: it is not real. Therefore, it vanishes when enquired into. It is best to reject the notion and stop it from arising again by never thinking of it again. There is neither the subject (seer) nor an experiencer, neither the real nor the unreal. There is the supreme peace alone. One who is established in this peace is free from likes and dislikes though engaged in activity. Or he may not engage himself in activity. When the mind is freed of all notions that limit the unconditioned consciousness, how does the sage act in a dualistic way? Free from love, hate and fear, he exists as the immutable self firmly established in the supreme peace.

"The notion of 'object' which arises in the 'subject' is then experienced by the latter as different from it. In fact, the two (like the dreamer and the wakeful person) are indistinguishably one, like milk that is kept in two cups. The supreme self is free from all notions. Notions give rise to objects and when the notions are abandoned the objects cease to be."

OṀ TAT SAṬ

the end and a beginning

RECOMMENDED BOOKS

The following books are recommended for further study:

(i) *Sadhana* by Swami Sivananda (from the Divine Life Society, P.O. Shivananda Nagar, Dt. Tehri-Garhwal, U.P., India.)

(ii) *Talks with Sri Ramana Maharishi* (from Sri Ramanasramam, Tiruvannamalai, South India.)

(iii) *Light on Yoga* by B.K.S. Iyengar (from George Allen and Unwin Ltd, London England.)

(iv) *Cit-sakti-vilasa* by Paramahamsa Muktananda (from Shree Gurudev Ashram, Ganeshpuri, P.O. Vajresvari, Dt. Thana, Maharashtra, India.)

(v) *The Awakening of Intelligence* by J. Krishnamurti (from Victor Gollancz Ltd., London, England.)

INDEX

YOGA ASANA PLATES

Stages 1 and 12

Stages
2 and 11

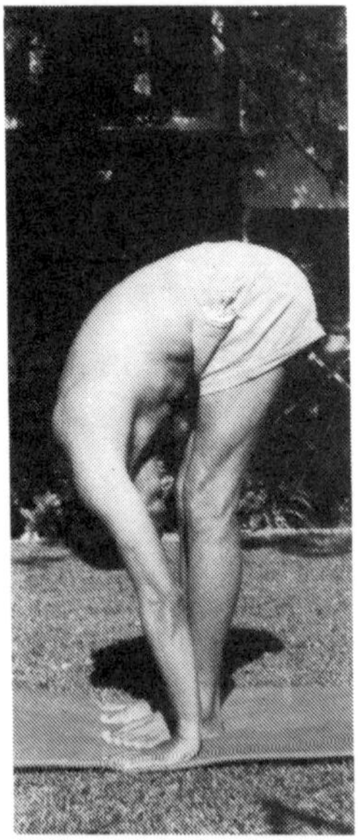

Stages 3 and 10

Stage 4

Stage 5

SURYANAMASKARA

(page 56)

Stage 6

Stage 7

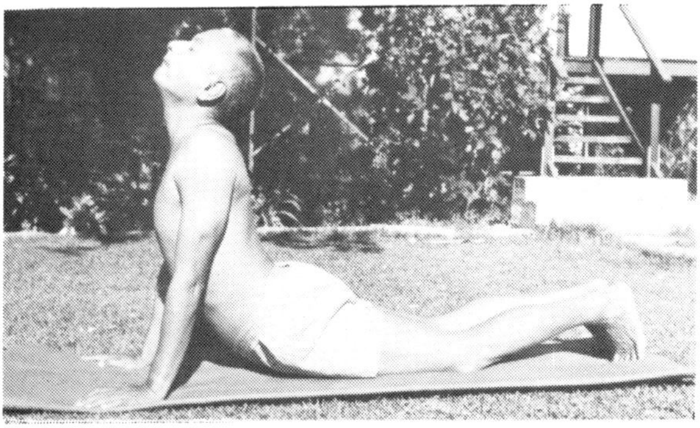

Stage 8

Stage 9

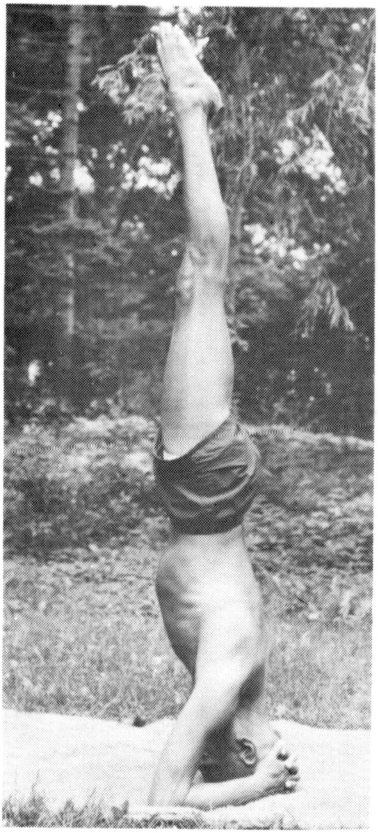

Sirasāsana
Head stand (page 58)

Sarvangāsana
Shoulder stand (page 60)

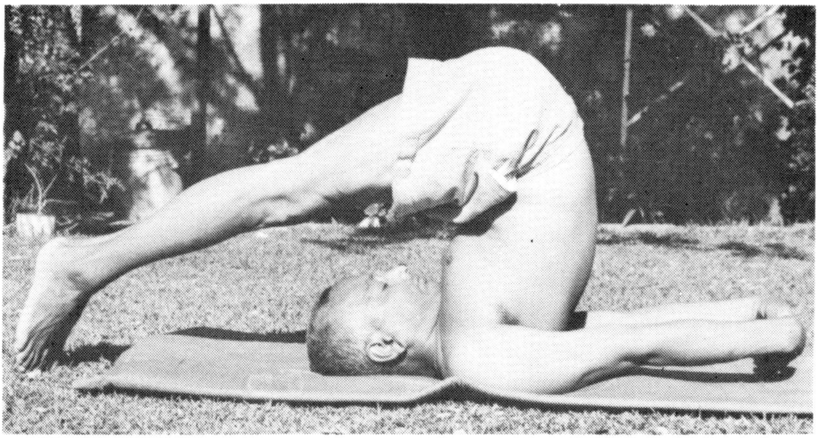

Halāsana
Plough posture (page 62)

Karṇapīḍāsana
Spider posture (page 64)
Variation of halasana

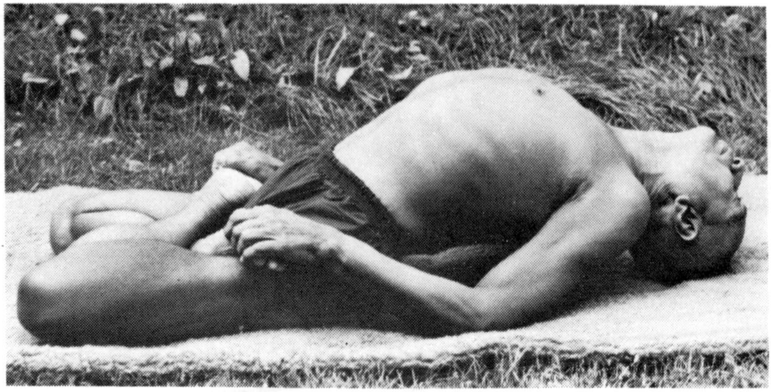

Matsyāsana
Fish posture (page 64)

It is possible to float on water in the matsyasana
Photo taken in Mauritius

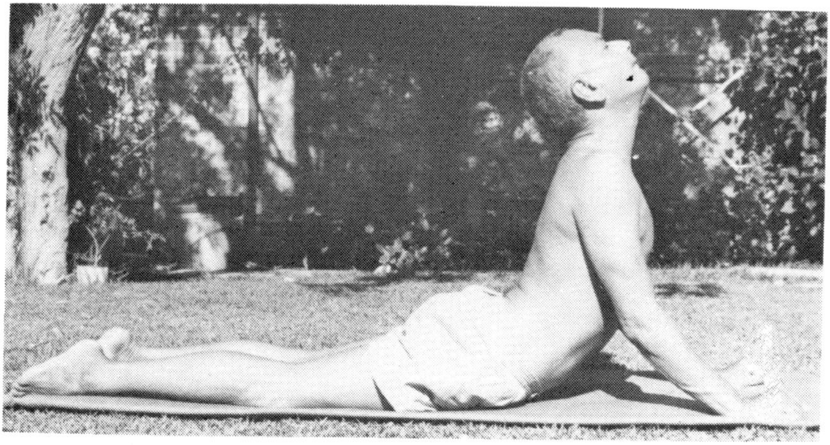

Bhujangāsana
Cobra posture (page 66)

Śalabhāsana
Locust posture (page 67)

Dhanurāsana
Bow posture (page 69)

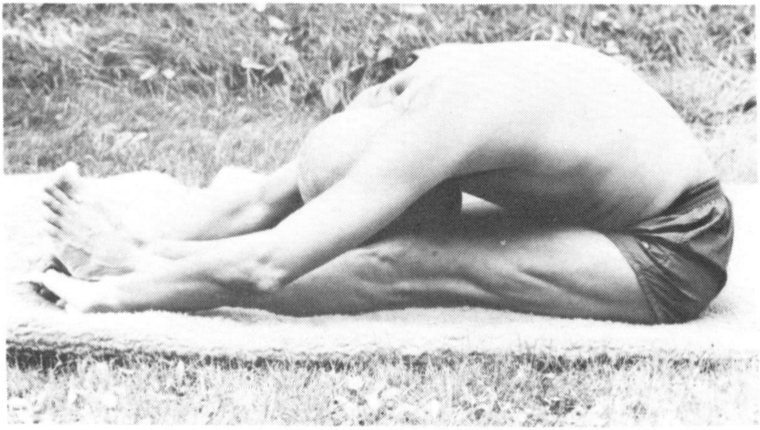

Paścimottānāsana
Forward bending posture (page 70)

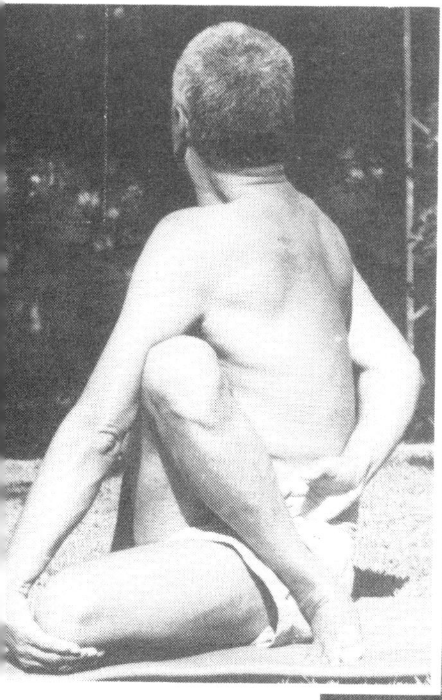

Ardhamatsyendrāsana
Spinal twist posture (page 72)

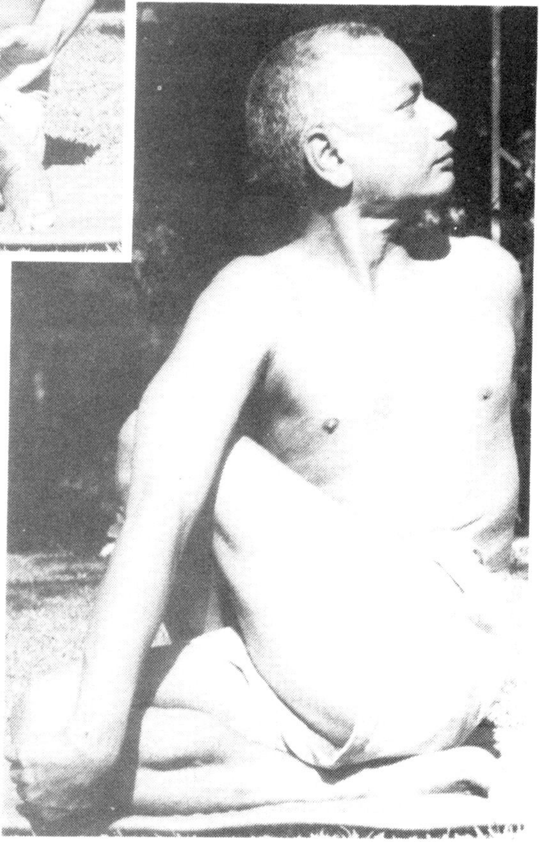

Trikonāsana
Triangle posture (page 78)

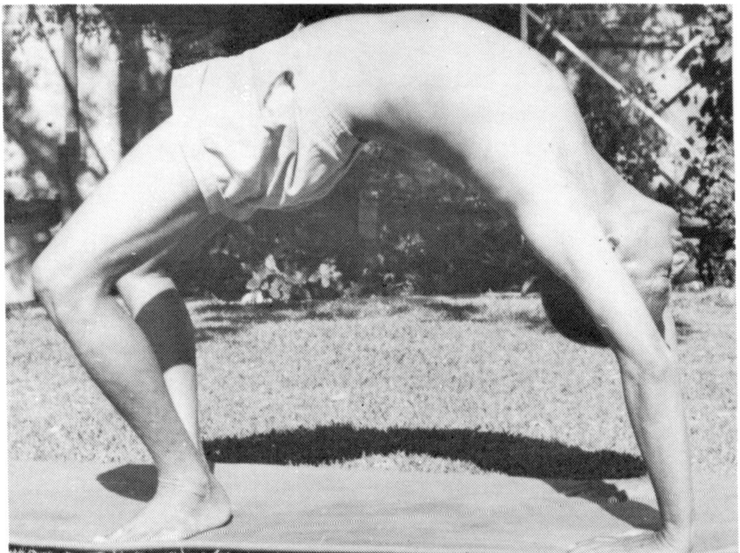

Cakrāsana
Bridge posture (page 77)

Mayūrāsana
Peacock posture (page 74)

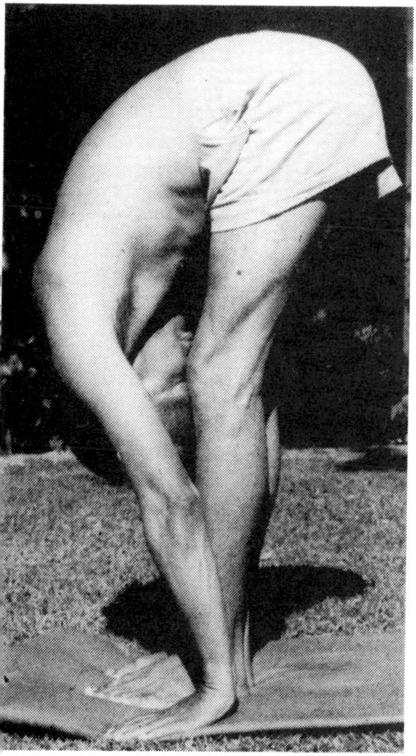

Pādahastāsana
Hand to feet posture
(page 77)

Padmāsana
Lotus posture (page 84)

Siddhāsana (page 83)

Variation of padmāsana

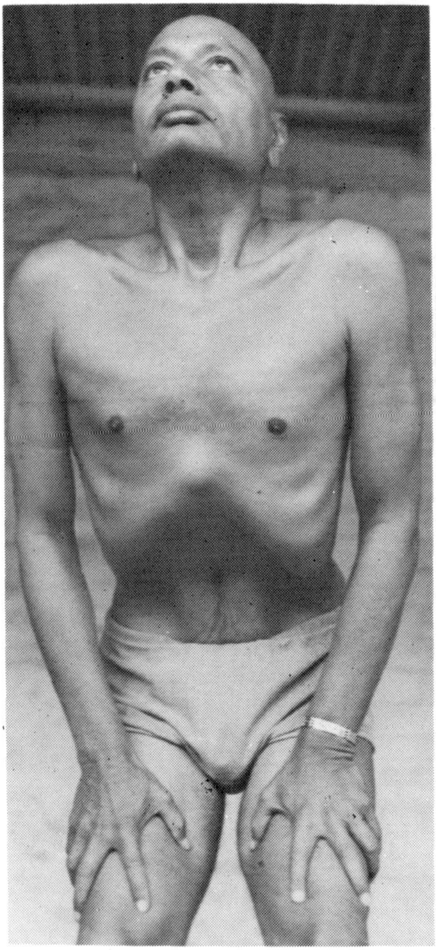

Nauli
Abdominal churning (page 79)

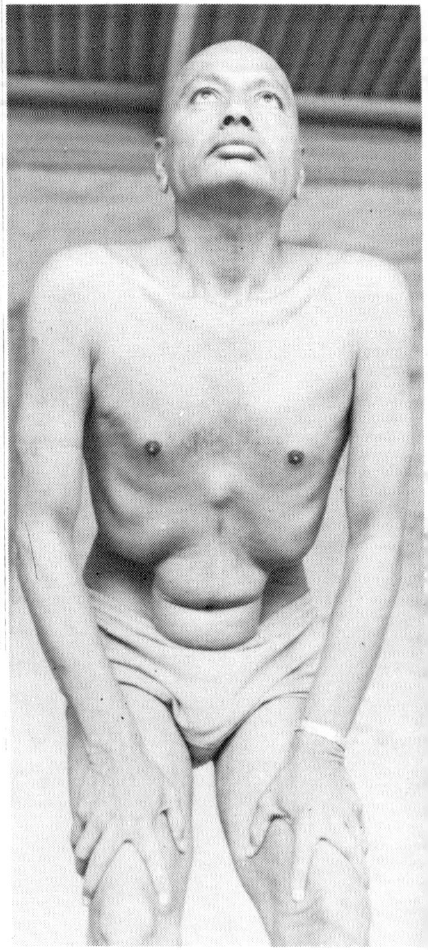

Uddīyāna
Abdominal lift (page 79)

Gomukhāsana (page 85)

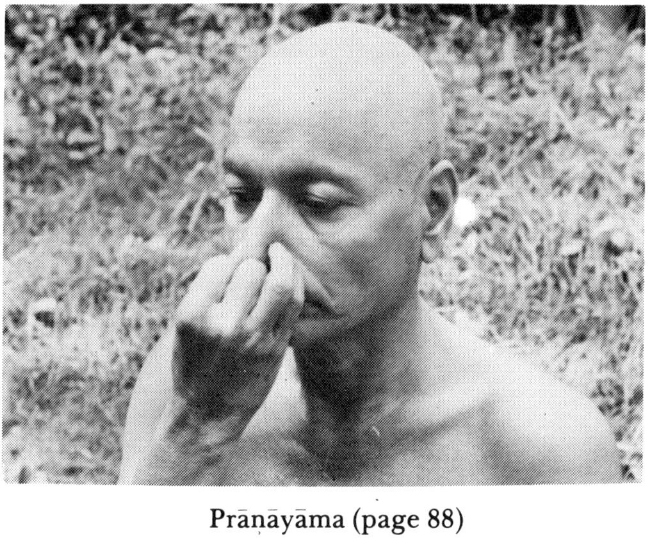

Prāṇāyāma (page 88)

Yoga mudrā
Yoga seal posture (page 101)

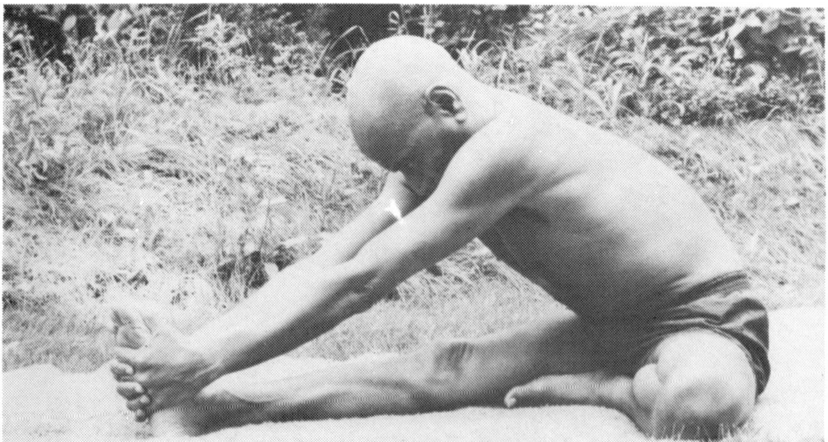

Mahā mudrā (page 101)

Bandha trāya
(page 104)

Yonī Mudrā
(page 105)

Concentration on the Ājña cakra
(page 121)

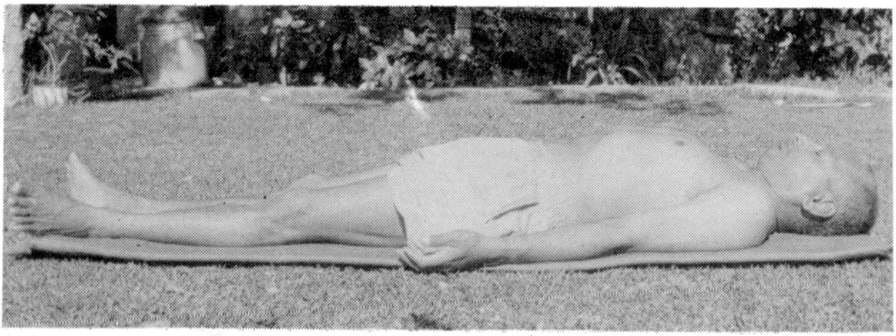

Śavāsana (page 80)

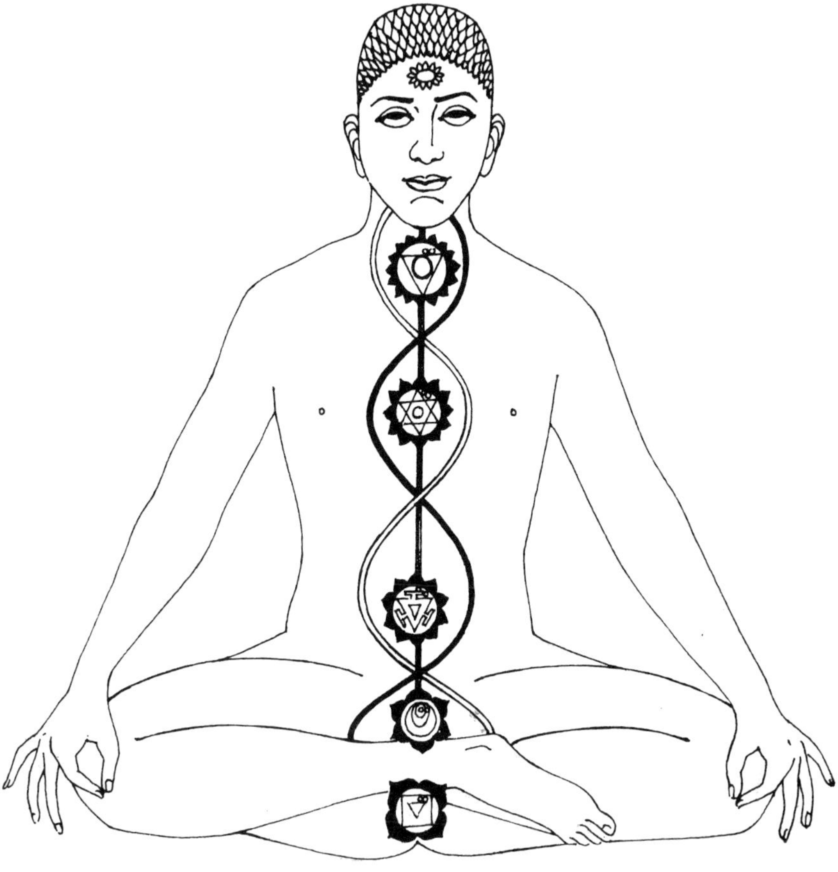

The Centres or Chakras

CATALOGUE

Swami Venkatesananda's books are voluntarily produced by trustees of the Chiltern Yoga Trust in Australia and Ananda Kutir in South Africa. The books are sold to cover costs and any profit is channelled back into the production of more.We hope to make this great sage and scholar's unique style of practical wisdom available to all who wish.

THE SUPREME YOGA *(Yoga Vasiṣṭha)*
This is one of the greatest and least known spiritual treasures of timeless India. In daily readings the text makes extensive use of stories and allegories to convey its profoundly metaphysical concepts. Regarded as 'the last word' in metaphysical teaching, it is the greatest help to spiritual awakening and the direct experience of the truth
366 pages 363 gm $19.50

THOUGHTS FOR TODAY (Venkatesa Daily Readings)
Short and concise - the quintessence of Swami Venkatesananda's teachings - piercing and thought provoking, each reading provides food for meditation.
397 pages 250gm $14.92

INSIGHTS AND INSPIRATIONS
Daily readings compiled from articles written by Swami Venkatesananda, in a style which is easy to read. His wisdom, humour and insight are made accessible to all readers.
Included are 100 photos of Swami taken at all ages and in different situations.
366 pages 573gm $24.95

THE YOGA SUTRAS OF PATANJALI
A commentary on the Yoga Sutras of Patanjali compiled from the many talks given by Swami Venkatesananda over the years. A lucid and masterly exposition of the Sutras.
400 pages 430gm $19.95

THE LOTUS AND THE ROSE
Lectures given by Swami Venkatesananda on Yoga and Christianity in 1982. An indepth look at these two major religions. In collaboration with Fr. Terence Melvin O.S.M.
180 pages 270 $11.95

MULTIPLE REFLECTIONS
This book of talks on the Yoga Vasistha is a wonderful introduction to its sublime philosophy.
162 pages 250gm $11.95

TALKS ON YOGA I
An enlightening lecture series based on Patanjali's Yoga Sutras.
57 pages 75gm $5.95

*RAJA YOGA
Lectures on Raja Yoga with a comprehensive foreword by Baba Muktananda. Not a text book as such, but a handbook which contains just enough material to help an eager student take up the practice of yoga in earnest.
190 pages 178gm $11.95

TOTAL LOVE
Where is that love that is timeless? Who knows o it? In this beautifully presented litle book one can really begin to understand the nature of that intangible essence we call love.
76 pages 113gm $8.95

*PHILOSOPHY, PSYCHOLOGY AND PRACTICE OF YOGA
In this book Swami Venkatesananda bridges the gap between Eastern and Western thought by exploring their common ground. His clarity of thought and lucid style, and his knack of explaining the most difficult concepts in the simplest way, make this book a joyous communication.
184 pages 150gm $11.95

FROM THE RIDICULOUS TO THE SUBLIME
Gems of wit and wiosdom gathered by Alison Salter from talks and discussions with Swami Venkatesananda in New Zealand.
64 pages $8.95 100gm

THE ETERNAL RELIGION
A book on Hinduism for the serious seeker and those interested in comparative religion.
240 pages $13.95 306gm

*SIVANANDA YOGA
Swami Venkatesananda's lectures given in Rishikesh in 1982. Revealing insights into the guru-disciple relationship. Relates how Swami Sivananda used simple everyday situations to train his disciples.
160 pages 134gm $11.95

TRUTH ETERNAL
Inspiring quotations from the Bible and the Bhagavad Gita illustrating the oneness of each concept. A commentary on each page containing insights culled from the teachings of Swami Venkatesananda. Compiled by Narayani.
132 pages 197gm $10.95

MANTRAS
This booklet contains the Sri Venkatesa Stotram, Prapattih and Mangalasasanam; Venkatesa Puja, Guru Pada Puja and Havan. The chants are in transliterated Sanskrit with brief explanations in English for those wishing to do puja and havan.
37 pages 75gm $5.95

*Books produced in India

AVAILABLE IN 2002

THE SONG OF GOD *(Bhagavad Gita)*
In daily readings, this translation of the classical dialogue between Sri Krishna and Arjuna on the battlefield of Kurukshetra with Swami's illuminating commentary makes this unique scripture available to all.

SIVANANDA DAILY READINGS
Readings from the works of Swami Sivananda, the greatest Indian sage of the century. Each reading is a pearl of wisdom to inspire and uplift every aspect of our lives.

AUDIO TAPES AND VIDEOS AVAILABLE ON REQUEST

Available from

The Chiltern Yoga Trust (Aust)
P. 0. Box 2, South Fremantle 6162
Western Australia

Ananda Kutir Yoga Association
P.O. Box 36134, Glosderry 7702
Cape Town, South Africa

PLEASE INCLUDE POSTAGE WITH YOUR ORDER.